CALIFORNIA

McDougal Littell

GEOMETRY

Larson   Boswell   Kanold   Stiff

California Standards Review and Practice

The California Standards Review and Practice book begins with in-depth review and practice of every California Geometry Standard. This is followed by an intensive cumulative review with mixed practice. A pretest and posttest covering the Geometry standards are included with the intensive review. All exercises are in multiple-choice format.

 **McDougal Littell**
A DIVISION OF HOUGHTON MIFFLIN COMPANY
Evanston, Illinois • Boston • Dallas

Cover photo: Death Valley © Jupiterimages Corporation

ISBN 13: 978-0-547-12447-6
ISBN 10: 0-547-12447-3

6 7 8 9 0868 15 14 13 12 11
4500325340   ABCDEFG

Contents

In-Depth Standards Review and Practice

Intensive Standards Review and Practice

California Geometry Mathematics Standards

As you read and study your mathematics textbook this year, you will be learning many of the ideas described in the California Mathematics Standards. The Geometry Standards that you will concentrate on are listed below.

Following each standard is an explanation of what it means and how you will learn about it. By the end of the year, you will have learned the content of these California Geometry Mathematics Standards.

	Geometry Standard	What It Means to You
1.0	Students demonstrate understanding by identifying and giving examples of undefined terms, axioms, theorems, and inductive and deductive reasoning.	You will learn about the basic terms and types of rules used in Geometry. You will also learn how to apply inductive and deductive reasoning to draw conclusions and create new rules. When you make a conjecture based on several examples, you are using inductive reasoning. Your conjecture may or may not be true. For example, you will prove a conjecture about the growth in the number of person-to-person e-mail messages sent each year. When you come to a conclusion based on statements that have been proven true, you are using deductive reasoning.
2.0	Students write geometric proofs, including proofs by contradiction.	The study of Geometry requires laying a foundation of rules. Then you will build upon these rules to create new rules. This building process is the writing of geometric proofs. You will learn how to write a direct proof, where you reason logically from what you know to what you want to prove. You will also learn how to write a proof by contradiction, where you reason from what you know and the opposite of what you want to prove until you arrive at a contradiction.
3.0	Students construct and judge the validity of a logical argument and give counterexamples to disprove a statement.	You will learn to identify the hypothesis and the conclusion in a statement, and to write conditional statements in if-then form. You will use the related conditionals—converse, inverse and contrapositive—to determine the validity of conjectures about Geometry. You will also learn that you can prove that a statement is false by providing one counterexample. For example, you will find a counterexample for the statement $(a + b)^2 = a^2 + b^2$.
4.0	Students prove basic theorems involving congruence and similarity.	You will learn about congruence of line segments and angles, and how it differs from equality. You will then use segment and angle congruence to solve problems involving congruent and similar geometric figures. For example, you will estimate the radius of the moon using similar triangles.
5.0	Students prove that triangles are congruent or similar, and they are able to use the concept of corresponding parts of congruent triangles.	Now that you have been introduced to congruence and similarity, you will focus on applying these concepts to triangles. You will learn how to use the SSS, SAS, and ASA Congruence Postulates to prove that two triangles are congruent. You will also use the ASA Congruence Postulate to prove the AAS Congruence Theorem, and you will use the HL Congruence Theorem to prove that two right triangles are congruent. The AA Similarity Postulate will allow you to prove the SSS and SAS Similarity Theorems. You will use similar triangles to estimate the height of a tall object, such as a tree.

Geometry Standard		What It Means to You
6.0	Students know and are able to use the triangle inequality theorem.	You will learn how the relationships between the lengths of sides in a triangle are restricted by the Triangle Inequality Theorem. You will prove this theorem and then use it to solve problems. For example, you will find the range of possible values for the distance between two points of interest in Washington, D.C.
7.0	Students prove and use theorems involving the properties of parallel lines cut by a transversal, the properties of quadrilaterals, and the properties of circles.	You will use what you know about angle congruence and supplementary angles to prove theorems about the congruence of angles formed when a transversal intersects a pair of parallel lines. You will use these theorems to determine how a robot keeps its foot flat on the floor when it moves. Then you will investigate the properties of general and special parallelograms, as well as trapezoids and kites. Parallelograms are used to model the motion of an amusement park ride. You will also begin an exploration of circles by learning about their basic properties.
8.0	Students know, derive, and solve problems involving the perimeter, circumference, area, volume, lateral area, and surface area of common geometric figures.	You will learn how the different types of measurement apply to geometric figures. Perimeter, circumference, and area are used to measure two-dimensional objects. Volume measures the space within a three-dimensional object. Lateral area is a measurement of the area of the "sides" of a solid object, excluding the top and bottom. Surface area measures the entire area of the surface of a solid object. You will use all these concepts in various application problems, such as finding the circumferences of Saturn's rings, calculating the amount of shrink wrap needed to wrap a product, and finding the volume of a sculpture.
9.0	Students compute the volumes and surface areas of prisms, pyramids, cylinders, cones, and spheres; and students commit to memory the formulas for prisms, pyramids, and cylinders.	You will learn how to find the volume and surface area of more complex three-dimensional shapes. Prisms, pyramids, cylinders, cones, and spheres occur frequently in the real world, and you will use the formulas from this standard to solve problems. For example, you will find the volume of an unusual geological feature, the size of the base of an Egyptian pyramid, and the probability of a meteorite strike in Earth's Torrid Zone.
10.0	Students compute areas of polygons, including rectangles, scalene triangles, equilateral triangles, rhombi, parallelograms, and trapezoids.	You will derive the formulas for standard polygons, and apply the formulas to solving a wide range of problems. For example, you will calculate the amount of paint need to cover a large area and find the areas of parts of a basketball court.
11.0	Students determine how changes in dimensions affect the perimeter, area, and volume of common geometric figures and solids.	You will investigate the effect on figures and solids when some or all of the dimensions change. Perimeter is a linear measurement and it changes with the same ratio as the change in dimensions. Area is a two-dimensional measurement and it changes with the square of the ratio of the change in dimensions. As a three-dimensional measurement, volume changes with the cube of the ratio of the change in dimensions. You will encounter these applications while learning about this topic: comparing swimming pools, using floor plans, constructing models, and comparing consumer items to find the better buy.

Geometry Standard		What It Means to You
12.0	Students find and use measures of sides and of interior and exterior angles of triangles and polygons to classify figures and solve problems.	You will learn about the relationships between the angle measures in triangles and polygons. This knowledge will help you classify polygons by number of sides and find the measures of unknown angles. It will help you determine if a triangle is scalene, isosceles, or equilateral. You will also use the Pythagorean theorem to prove theorems about the relationships between side lengths in triangles. You will then be able to classify triangles as right, acute, or obtuse, based on their side lengths. For example, you will develop a method to determine if a catamaran mast is perpendicular to its deck.
13.0	Students prove relationships between angles in polygons by using properties of complementary, supplementary, vertical, and exterior angles.	You will apply your knowledge of complementary angles, supplementary angles, vertical angles, external angles, isosceles triangles, right triangles, and other theorems you have learned previously, to prove relationships between angles in polygons.
14.0	Students prove the Pythagorean theorem.	You will investigate different ways to prove the Pythagorean theorem, which defines the relationship that exists between the lengths of the sides of any right triangle and the length of its hypotenuse.
15.0	Students use the Pythagorean theorem to determine distance and find missing lengths of sides of right triangles.	You will use the Pythagorean theorem to find unknown lengths in problems containing right triangles. You will solve problems involving side lengths, diagonals, perimeters, and areas. For example, you will calculate dimensions in architectural objects, distances in a baseball diamond, and the shortest path to a campsite.
16.0	Students perform basic constructions with a straightedge and compass, such as angle bisectors, perpendicular bisectors, and the line parallel to a given line through a point off the line.	You will learn about constructions, which are geometric drawings that use a limited set of tools, usually a compass and a straightedge. Once you learn to construct basic geometric figures, you will have a better understanding of many geometric proofs. For example, you will construct parallel lines, parallelograms, perpendicular lines, congruent line segments, congruent angles, medians, and similar figures.
17.0	Students prove theorems by using coordinate geometry, including the midpoint of a line segment, the distance formula, and various forms of equations of lines and circles.	You will graph geometric figures on a coordinate plane. You will then apply the definition of slope to prove whether lines are parallel, perpendicular, or neither. You will also use formulas to find the distance between two points and the point that lies halfway between them. These concepts will allow you to prove theorems you have learned previously, using the coordinates of relevant points in figures graphed on a coordinate plane.
18.0	Students know the definitions of the basic trigonometric functions defined by the angles of a right triangle. They also know and are able to use elementary relationships between them. For example, $\tan(x) = \dfrac{\sin(x)}{\cos(x)}$, $(\sin(x))^2 + (\cos(x))^2 = 1$.	Your will learn about the trigonometric functions that apply to every right triangle. You will use the sine, cosine, and tangent ratios to describe the relationship between the sides of a right triangle. You will also learn about some important trigonometric identities.

Geometry Standard		What It Means to You
19.0	Students use trigonometric functions to solve for an unknown length of a side of a right triangle, given an angle and a length of a side.	You will use the trigonometric ratios of sine, cosine, and tangent to find the length of one side of a right triangle when you know the length of one other side and the measure of one of the acute angles. This will allow you to solve many real-world problems involving right triangles. You will use trigonometric ratios to find the height of the Washington Monument, the dimensions of a skateboard ramp, and the distance down a skiing trail.
20.0	Students know and are able to use angle and side relationships in problems with special right triangles, such as 30°, 60°, and 90° triangles and 45°, 45°, and 90° triangles.	You will learn how to find side lengths in right triangles with special properties. You will focus on right triangles with two angles of 45°, and on right triangles with angles of 30° and 60°. You will see that some common application problems involve equilateral triangles drawn with an altitude. An altitude divides an equilateral triangle into two triangles with angles of 30°, 60°, and 90°. You will use special right triangles to find the height of a drawbridge, and also to calculate the size and shape of fabric squares used to make a quilt.
21.0	Students prove and solve problems regarding relationships among chords, secants, tangents, inscribed angles, and inscribed and circumscribed polygons of circles.	You will learn about the relationship between circles and various types of lines that intersect them, such as chords, tangents, secants and diameters. The intersections of these lines with each other and with circles result in angles, arcs, inscribed angles, and intercepted arcs, all of which are interrelated. You will learn about polygons inscribed in circles, which are polygons that fit inside circles in a certain way. You will also learn about polygons that circumscribe circles, which are polygons that surround circles in a certain way. Some problems you will solve include identifying the range of a GPS satellite, calculating the speed of a car based on tire marks, finding the correct location for taking a photograph, and estimating the part of Earth from which the Northern Lights can be seen.
22.0	Students know the effect of rigid motions on figures in the coordinate plane and space, including rotations, translations, and reflections.	You will learn rules for ways to transform a figure, such as rotation, translation, and reflection. A rotation involves moving a figure about a point through an angle. A translation is a shifting of an object in a vertical and/or horizontal direction. A reflection creates a mirror image of a figure across a line of reflection. You will use transformations to create patterns in fabrics and floors, to find an optimal parking spot, and to analyze the motion of a revolving door.

California Standards Review
and Practice
In-Depth Review

California Standards
Geometry 1.0

Students demonstrate understanding by identifying and giving examples of undefined terms, axioms, theorems, and inductive and deductive reasoning.

Undefined Terms and Reasoning

Terms to Know	Example
Undefined terms are words that do not have formal definitions, but there is agreement about what they mean.	In geometry, the words *point*, *line*, and *plane* are undefined terms.
An **axiom,** or postulate, is a rule that is accepted without proof.	Postulate 5: Through any two points, there exists exactly one line.
A **theorem** is a rule that can be proven.	**Theorem 2.3** (Right Angles Congruence Theorem): All right angles are congruent.
You use **inductive reasoning** when you find a pattern in specific cases and then write a conjecture for the general case.	The next number in the pattern 　　7, 14, 21, . . . is 28.
Deductive reasoning uses facts, definitions, accepted properties, and the laws of logic to form a logical argument.	Sam practices the piano every Tuesday and Thursday. Today is Thursday. Therefore, Sam practices the piano today.

Example 1　　**Identify Undefined Terms**

Which of the following represents undefined terms?

a.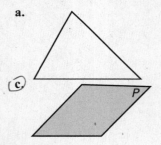

b.  m

c.

d.

P

Solution

a. A triangle can be described using known words such as *polygon* and *sides*. It is not an undefined term.

b. A line is an undefined term.

c. A plane is an undefined term.

d. A ray can be described using known words, such as *point* and *line*. It is not an undefined term.

Example 2 ## Inductive Reasoning

Describe how to sketch the next figure in the pattern. Then sketch the next figure.

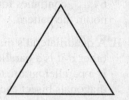 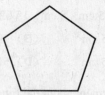 

Solution

Each figure has one more equal-length side and one more equal-measure angle than the figure before it.

Answer Sketch the next figure by drawing a figure with six equal-length sides and six equal-measure angles.

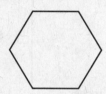

Example 3 ## Deductive Reasoning

Make a valid conclusion in the situation.

> If it rains or snows today, then the Biology field trip will be canceled. It is raining today.

Solution

Identify the hypothesis and the conclusion of the first statement. The hypothesis is "If it rains or snows today," and the conclusion is "then the Biology field trip will be canceled."

"It is raining today" satisfies the hypothesis of the conditional statement, so you can conclude that the Biology field trip will be canceled.

Answer The Biology field trip will be canceled.

Exercises

1. Look for the pattern in the figures shown below. How many squares will there be in the tenth figure?

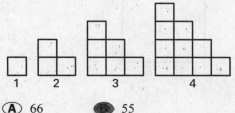

  (A) 66   (B) 55

  (C) 45   (D) 36

2. ∠1 and ∠2 are supplementary angles. Which of the following statements can be justified if $m\angle 1 = 110°$?

  (A) ∠2 is acute because measures of supplementary angles have a sum of 90°.

  ● ∠2 is acute because measures of supplementary angles have a sum of 180°.

  (C) ∠2 is obtuse because measures of supplementary angles have a sum of 180°.

  (D) ∠2 is right because measures of supplementary angles have a sum of 180°.

3. The list below shows the volumes of cubes as the length of the edges is increased. What is the volume of the eighth cube in the pattern?

1 cm^3, 3.375 cm^3, 8 cm^3, 15.625 cm^3, . . .

(A) 48.875 cm^3 (B) 79.1 cm^3

(C) 91.125 cm^3 (D) 512 cm^3

4. Which statement about the figures below must be true?

(A) The four figures are regular.

(B) The four figures are equilateral.

(C) The four figures are equiangular.

(D) The four figures are similar.

5. In isosceles trapezoid $ABCD$, $AB = 28$ inches and $DC = 48$ inches. What additional data does *not* provide sufficient information to find the area of the trapezoid?

(A) the perimeter of the trapezoid

(B) the length of $\overline{BC}$

(C) the measure of $\angle AED$

(D) the length of $\overline{AE}$

6. The table shows the dimensions of several rectangles that fit a pattern. What are the dimensions of another rectangle that fits the pattern?

Length	Width
45	40
50	36
60	30
75	24
90	20
100	18
120	15

(A) 80 by 42 (B) 72 by 25

(C) 70 by 68 (D) 65 by 58

7. Consider the arguments below.

I. The number pattern 1, 4, 9, 16, 25, 36, 49, 64, . . . continues forever. The number 800 is not in the pattern.

II. A quadrilateral's diagonals bisect each other if it is a parallelogram. A rectangle is a parallelogram, therefore a rectangle's diagonals bisect each other.

Which one(s), if any, use inductive reasoning?

(A) I only

(B) II only

(C) both I and II

(D) neither I nor II

8. Look for the pattern in the dimensions of the prisms shown below. What will be the volume of the next figure in the pattern?

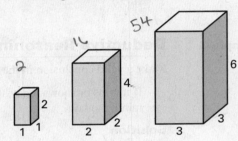

(A) 8 units^3 (B) 96 units^3

(C) 128 units^3 (D) 256 units^3

9. Which of the following does not represent an undefined term?

(A)  m

(B) $\bullet\, x$

(C)

(D)

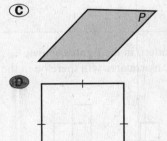

California Standards
Geometry 2.0

Students write geometric proofs, including proofs by contradiction.

Geometric Proofs

A **proof** is a logical argument that shows a statement is true.

Direct Proof	
STEP 1	Identify the given information and the statement you want to prove.
STEP 2	Reason logically from the given information, making one statement at a time, until you reach the conclusion.

Proof by Contradiction	
STEP 1	Identify the given information and the statement that you want to prove. Assume that this statement is false by assuming that its opposite is true.
STEP 2	Reason logically, making one statement at a time, until you reach a contradiction.
STEP 3	State that the desired conclusion must be true because the contradiction proves that the original assumption is false.

Example 1   **Write a Direct Proof**

GIVEN ▶ $AC = BD$
PROVE ▶ $AB = CD$

Solution

Statements	Reasons
1. $AC = BD$	1. Given
2. $AB + BC = AC$	2. Segment Addition Postulate
3. $BD = BC + CD$	3. Segment Addition Postulate
4. $AC = BC + CD$	4. Substitute AC for BD.
5. $AB + BC = BC + CD$	5. Transitive Property of Equality
6. $AB = CD$	6. Subtract BC from both sides.

Example 2

Write a Proof by Contradiction

GIVEN ▶ $m\angle A = 115°$
PROVE ▶ $\angle B$ is not a right angle.

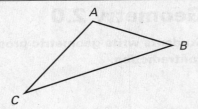

Solution

STEP 1 Assume that $\angle B$ is a right angle.

STEP 2 If $\angle B$ is a right angle, then the sum of the measures of the other two angles in the triangle must be 90°: $m\angle A + m\angle C = 90°$. Therefore $m\angle A = 90° - m\angle C$, so $m\angle A < 90°$. But $m\angle A = 115°$, which is a contradiction.

STEP 3 Therefore, the assumption that $\angle B$ is a right angle must be false, which proves that $\angle B$ is not a right angle.

Exercises

1. You are asked to prove the following by contradiction.

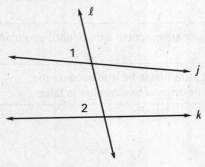

Given: $m\angle 2 \neq m\angle 1$

Prove: $j \nparallel k$

Which theorem or postulate will you use to reach a contradiction?

(A) Alternate Exterior Angles Theorem

(B) Corresponding Angles Postulate

(C) Consecutive Interior Angles Theorem

(D) Parallel Postulate

2. Use the proof to answer the question below.

Given: $\angle 1$ and $\angle 3$ are vertical angles.

Prove: $\angle 2 \cong \angle 4$

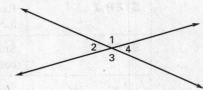

Statement	Reason
1. $\angle 1$ and $\angle 3$ are vertical angles.	1. Given
2. $\angle 2$ and $\angle 3$ are a linear pair. $\angle 3$ and $\angle 4$ are a linear pair.	2. Definition of linear pair, as shown in the diagram
3. $\angle 2$ and $\angle 3$ are supplementary. $\angle 3$ and $\angle 4$ are supplementary.	3. Linear Pair Postulate
4. $\angle 2 \cong \angle 4$	4. ?

Which reason can be used to justify Statement 4?

(A) Congruent Supplements Theorem

(B) Congruent Complements Theorem

(C) Symmetric Property of Angle Congruence

(D) Transitive Property of Angle Congruence

California Standard Geometry 2.0

3. In the figure below, $\angle 1 \not\cong \angle 2$ and $\overline{DE} \cong \overline{EF}$.

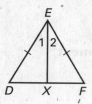

If we assume that $\overline{DX} \cong \overline{XF}$, and use $\overline{EX} \cong \overline{EX}$ by the Reflexive Property of Segment Congruence, then $\triangle DEX \cong \triangle FEX$ by SSS. We can conclude that $\angle 1 \cong \angle 2$ because corresponding parts of congruent triangles are congruent. This contradicts the given statement that $\angle 1 \not\cong \angle 2$. What conclusion can be drawn from this contradiction?

- **Ⓐ** $\angle 1 \cong \angle 2$
- **Ⓑ** $\angle 1 \not\cong \angle 1$
- **Ⓒ** $\overline{DX} \not\cong \overline{XF}$
- **Ⓓ** $\overline{DE} \not\cong \overline{EF}$

4. Given: $s \not\parallel t$

Prove: Lines s and t intersect at exactly one point.

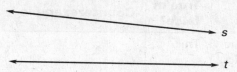

Consider the two assumptions.

I. Lines s and t intersect at more than one point.

II. Lines s and t do not intersect.

Which one(s), if any, would you use to write a proof by contradiction?

- **Ⓐ** I only
- **Ⓑ** II only
- **Ⓒ** both I and II
- **Ⓓ** neither I nor II

5. Use the proof to answer the question below.

Given: $\overline{AB} \cong \overline{CD}$, $\overline{CD} \cong \overline{EF}$

Prove: $\overline{AB} \cong \overline{EF}$

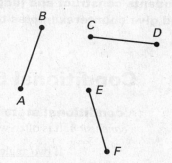

Statement	Reason
1. $\overline{AB} \cong \overline{CD}$; $\overline{CD} \cong \overline{EF}$	1. Given
2. $AB = CD$; $CD = EF$	2. Definition of congruent segments
3. $AB = EF$	3. ?
4. $\overline{AB} \cong \overline{EF}$	4. Definition of congruent segments

Which reason can be used to justify Statement 3?

- **Ⓐ** Symmetric Property
- **Ⓑ** Transitive Property
- **Ⓒ** Reflexive Property
- **Ⓓ** Ruler Postulate

6. Susan wants to prove that the hypotenuse of a right triangle is the longest side. What assumption should she make to write a proof by contradiction?

- **Ⓐ** $PR + RQ > PQ$
- **Ⓑ** $PR + RQ < PQ$
- **Ⓒ** $PR < PQ$ and $RQ < PQ$
- **Ⓓ** $PR > PQ$ or $RQ > PQ$

California Standards
Geometry 3.0

Students construct and judge the validity of a logical argument and give counterexamples to disprove a statement.

Conditional Statements and Counterexamples

A **conditional statement** is a logical statement made up of a *hypothesis* and a *conclusion*. It is often written in if-then form:

If <u>two angles are both right angles</u>, then <u>they are congruent</u>.

↑ hypothesis   ↑ conclusion

Conditional statements can be either true or false. If you want to show that a conditional statement is true, then you must prove that the conclusion is true whenever the hypothesis is true. If you want to show that a conditional statement is false, you need to give only one *counterexample*. A **counterexample** is a specific case for which the hypothesis is true but the conclusion is false.

By rearranging or negating the hypothesis and conclusion of a conditional statement, you can form related conditionals.

Related Conditional	Example	True or false?	Counterexample
Conditional statement	If two angles are both right angles, then they are congruent.	True	
Converse Exchange the hypothesis and the conclusion.	If two angles are congruent, then they are both right angles.	False	
Inverse Negate both the hypothesis and the conclusion.	If two angles are not both right angles, then they are not congruent.	False	
Contrapositive Write the converse, then negate both the hypothesis and the conclusion.	If two angles are not congruent, then they are not both right angles.	True	

A conditional statement and its contrapositive are either both true or both false. Also, the converse and the inverse of a conditional statement are either both true or both false.

Example 1   **Analyze Conditional Statements**

Write the if-then form, the converse, the inverse, and the contrapositive of the conditional statement. Decide whether each statement is *true* or *false*.

Parallelograms are quadrilaterals.

Solution

If-then form: *If a figure is a parallelogram, then it is a quadrilateral.*
A parallelogram is a quadrilateral. The statement is true.

Converse: Exchange the hypothesis and the conclusion.
If a figure is a quadrilateral, then it is a parallelogram.

Counterexample: A trapezoid is a quadrilateral, but it is not a parallelogram. The statement is false.

Inverse: Negate both the hypothesis and the conclusion.
If a figure is not a parallelogram, then it is not a quadrilateral.

Counterexample: A trapezoid is not a parallelogram, but it is a quadrilateral. The statement is false.

Contrapositive: Write the converse.
If a figure is a quadrilateral, then it is a parallelogram.
Negate both the hypothesis and the conclusion.
If a figure is not a quadrilateral, then it is not a parallelogram.

If a figure does not have four sides, it can't be a parallelogram. The statement is true.

Example 2   **Find Counterexamples**

Show that the conjecture is false by finding a counterexample.

a. If $JK = KL$, then K is the midpoint of $\overline{JL}$.

b. If $AB = BC = CD = DA$, then quadrilateral $ABCD$ is a square.

Solution

a. J, K, and L do not have to be collinear.

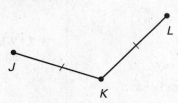

b. Quadrilateral $ABCD$ may not have a right angle.

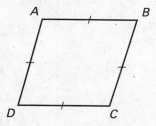

Exercises

California Standard
Geometry 3.0

Identify the statement that has the same meaning as the given statement.

1. The seafood restaurant is closed every Monday.

    A If the seafood restaurant is closed, then it is Monday.

    B If it is Monday, then the seafood restaurant is not closed.

    C If it is Monday, then the seafood restaurant is closed.

    D If it is not Monday, then the seafood restaurant is not closed.

2. You can buy a new CD once you have saved enough money.

    A If you have saved enough money, then you can buy a new CD.

    B If you can't buy a new CD, then you have saved enough money.

    C If you have not saved enough money, then you can buy a new CD.

    D If you buy a new CD, then you have not saved enough money.

3. You are told that a conditional statement is false.

Consider the related conditionals.

    I. Inverse

    II. Contrapositive

    III. Converse

Which one(s) is (are) also false?

    A I only   **B** II only

    C III only   **D** both I and III

4. *"Through any three points there exists exactly one plane."*

Which of the following best describes a counterexample to the conjecture above?

    A parallel planes

    B perpendicular lines

    C collinear points

    D parallel lines

5. If $DEFG$ is a parallelogram with diagonals $\overline{DF}$ and $\overline{EG}$, which of the following *must* be true?

    A $DF = EG$ **B** $\overline{DF}$ bisects $\overline{EG}$.

    C $DE = DG$ **D** $\overline{DE} \perp \overline{DG}$

6. A conditional statement is shown below.

> If $\angle 1$ and $\angle 2$ are complementary, then they form a right angle.

Which of the following is a counterexample to the statement?

    A
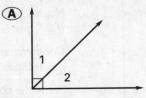

    B
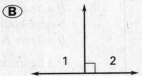

    C
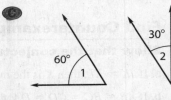

    D
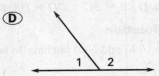

7. Which statement is sufficient to prove that $\angle 1$ and $\angle 2$ are complementary?

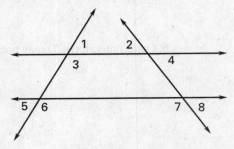

    A $\angle 1$ and $\angle 6$ are supplementary.

    B $\angle 2$ and $\angle 4$ are complementary.

    C $\angle 1$ and $\angle 7$ are supplementary.

    D $\angle 5$ and $\angle 8$ are complementary.

Name _____   Date _____

California Standards
Geometry 4.0

Students prove basic theorems involving congruence and similarity.

Congruence and Similarity

Terms to Know	Example
Two line segments are **congruent segments** if they have the same length.	$AB = CD$ ("is equal to") $\overline{AB} \cong \overline{CD}$ ("is congruent to")
Two angles are **congruent angles** if they have the same measure.	$m\angle A = m\angle B$ ("is equal to") $\angle A \cong \angle B$ ("is congruent to")
Two geometric figures are **congruent** if they have exactly the same size and shape.	Same size and shape
Two polygons are **similar polygons** if corresponding angles are congruent and corresponding side lengths are proportional.	$ABCD \sim EFGH$ Corresponding angles: $\angle A \cong \angle E$, $\angle B \cong \angle F$, $\angle C \cong \angle G$, $\angle D \cong \angle H$ Ratio of corresponding sides: $\dfrac{AB}{EF} = \dfrac{BC}{FG} = \dfrac{CD}{GH} = \dfrac{DA}{HE}$

Congruence of Segments and Angles	Example
Segment and angle congruence are reflexive, symmetric, and transitive.	
Reflexive	For any segment AB, $\overline{AB} \cong \overline{AB}$. For any angle A, $\angle A \cong \angle A$.
Symmetric	If $\overline{AB} \cong \overline{CD}$, then $\overline{CD} \cong \overline{AB}$. If $\angle A \cong \angle B$, then $\angle B \cong \angle A$.
Transitive	If $\overline{AB} \cong \overline{CD}$ and $\overline{CD} \cong \overline{EF}$, then $\overline{AB} \cong \overline{EF}$. If $\angle A \cong \angle B$ and $\angle B \cong \angle C$, then $\angle A \cong \angle C$.

Angle Congruence Theorems

Congruent Supplements Theorem

If two angles are supplementary to the same angle (or to congruent angles), then they are congruent.

If $\angle 1$ and $\angle 2$ are supplementary and $\angle 2$ and $\angle 3$ are supplementary, then $\angle 1 \cong \angle 3$.

Congruent Complements Theorem

If two angles are complementary to the same angle (or to congruent angles), then they are congruent.

If $\angle 4$ and $\angle 5$ are complementary and $\angle 6$ and $\angle 5$ are complementary, then $\angle 4 \cong \angle 6$.

Vertical Angles Congruence Theorem

Vertical angles are congruent.

$\angle 1 \cong \angle 3, \angle 2 \cong \angle 4$

Example 1

Congruence

GIVEN ▶ $\overrightarrow{PR}$ bisects $\angle QPS$.

$\overrightarrow{PS}$ bisects $\angle RPT$.

PROVE ▶ $\angle QPR \cong \angle SPT$

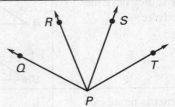

Solution

Statements	Reasons
1. $\overrightarrow{PR}$ bisects $\angle QPS$. $\overrightarrow{PS}$ bisects $\angle RPT$.	1. Given
2. $\angle QPR \cong \angle RPS$	2. Definition of Angle Bisector
3. $\angle RPS \cong \angle SPT$	3. Definition of Angle Bisector
4. $\angle QPR \cong \angle SPT$	4. Transitive Property of Angle Congruence

Example 2

Similarity

In the diagram, $\triangle PQR \sim \triangle STU$. Find the value of x.

Solution

The triangles are similar, so the corresponding side lengths are proportional.

$$\frac{PR}{PQ} = \frac{SU}{ST} \qquad \textbf{Write a proportion.}$$

$$\frac{18}{21} = \frac{12}{x} \qquad \textbf{Substitute.}$$

$$18x = 252 \qquad \textbf{Cross Products Property}$$

$$x = 14 \qquad \textbf{Solve for } x.$$

Exercises

1. Determine which pair of triangles is similar.

(A) two scalene triangles

(B) two isosceles triangles

(C) two right triangles

(●) two equilateral triangles

2. In the diagram, $\triangle ABC \sim \triangle EDF$. What is the value of y?

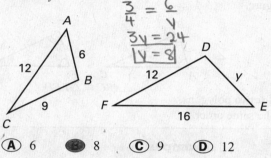

$$\frac{3}{4} = \frac{6}{y}$$
$$3y = 24$$
$$y = 8$$

(A) 6   (●) 8   (C) 9   (D) 12

3. In the figure below, $m\angle CFD = 90°$.

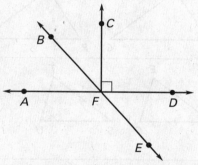

Which pair of angles cannot be proven congruent?

(●) $\angle BFC, \angle EFD$ (B) $\angle AFB, \angle EFD$

(C) $\angle CFD, \angle CFA$ (D) $\angle AFE, \angle BFD$

4. Which statement about the figure is *not true*?

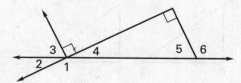

(A) $\angle 3$ and $\angle 6$ are supplementary.

(●) $\angle 1$ and $\angle 5$ are supplementary.

(C) $\angle 3$ and $\angle 4$ are complementary.

(D) $\angle 2$ and $\angle 5$ are complementary.

5. In the figure, $\triangle PQR \sim \triangle XYZ$. Which statement must be true?

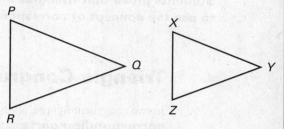

(A) The two triangles are isosceles.

(B) The two triangles are congruent.

(C) The corresponding sides of the two triangles are congruent.

(●) The corresponding angles of the two triangles are congruent.

6. Use the proof to answer the question below.

Given: $\angle WVY$ and $\angle XVZ$ are right angles.

Prove: $\angle YVZ \cong \angle WVX$

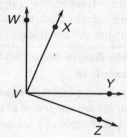

Statement	**Reason**
1. $\angle WVY$ and $\angle XVZ$ are right angles.	1. Given
2. $\angle WVH$ and $\angle XVY$ are complementary.	2. Definition of complementary angles
3. $\angle WVY$ and $\angle YVZ$ are complementary.	3. Definition of complementary angles
4. $\angle YVY \cong \angle WVX$	4. ?

Which reason can be used to justify Statement 4?

(A) Vertical Angles Congruence Theorem

(●) Symmetric Property of Congruent Angles

(C) Congruent Complements Theorem

(D) Congruent Supplements Theorem

California Standard Geometry 4.0

California Standards
Geometry 5.0

Students prove that triangles are congruent or similar, and they are able to use the concept of corresponding parts of congruent triangles.

Triangle Congruence and Similarity

In two congruent figures, all the parts of one figure are congruent to the **corresponding parts** of the other figure.

Corresponding angles:
$\angle A \cong \angle F$, $\angle B \cong \angle E$, $\angle C \cong \angle D$

Corresponding sides:
$\overline{AB} \cong \overline{FE}$, $\overline{BC} \cong \overline{ED}$, $\overline{AC} \cong \overline{FD}$

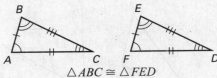

$\triangle ABC \cong \triangle FED$

When you write a congruence statement for two polygons, always list the corresponding vertices in the same order.

Triangle Congruence	Example
Side-Side-Side (SSS) Congruence Postulate If three sides of one triangle are congruent to three sides of a second triangle, then the two triangles are congruent. $\triangle ABC \cong \triangle PQR$	
Side-Angle-Side (SAS) Congruence Postulate If two sides and the included angle of one triangle are congruent to two sides and the included angle of a second triangle, then the two triangles are congruent. $\triangle DEF \cong \triangle STU$	
Angle-Side-Angle (ASA) Congruence Postulate If two angles and the included side of one triangle are congruent to two angles and the included side of a second triangle, then the two triangles are congruent. $\triangle DEF \cong \triangle MNO$	
Hypotenuse-Leg (HL) Congruence Theorem If the hypotenuse and a leg of a right triangle are congruent to the hypotenuse and a leg of a second right triangle, then the two triangles are congruent. $\triangle JKL \cong \triangle XYZ$	
Angle-Angle-Side (AAS) Congruence Theorem If two angles and a non-included side of one triangle are congruent to two angles and a non-included side of a second triangle, then the two triangles are congruent. $\triangle GHI \cong \triangle VWX$	

Copyright © by McDougal Littell, a division of Houghton Mifflin Company.

Triangle Similarity	Example
Angle-Angle (AA) Similarity Postulate If two angles of one triangle are congruent to two angles of another triangle, then the two triangles are similar. $\triangle JKL \sim \triangle PQR$	
Side-Side-Side (SSS) Similarity Theorem If the corresponding side lengths of two triangles are proportional, then the triangles are similar. $\dfrac{AB}{JK} = \dfrac{BC}{KL} = \dfrac{AC}{JL};\ \triangle ABC \sim \triangle JKL$	
Side-Angle-Side (SAS) Similarity Theorem If an angle of one triangle is congruent to an angle of a second triangle and the lengths of the sides including these angles are proportional, then the triangles are similar. $\dfrac{SU}{MO} = \dfrac{ST}{MN};\ \triangle STU \sim \triangle MNO$	

Example 1

Prove Triangles Are Congruent

Write a proof.

GIVEN ▶ M is the midpoint of $\overline{AC}$.
M is the midpoint of $\overline{BD}$.

PROVE ▶ $\triangle AMB \cong \triangle CMD$

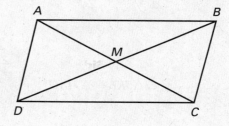

Solution

Statements	Reasons
1. M is the midpoint of $\overline{AC}$. M is the midpoint of $\overline{BD}$.	1. Given
2. $\overline{AM} \cong \overline{MC}$ $\overline{BM} \cong \overline{MD}$	2. Definition of Segment Midpoint
3. $\angle AMB \cong \angle CMD$	3. Vertical Angles Congruence Theorem
4. $\triangle AMB \cong \triangle CMD$	4. SAS Congruence Postulate

Example 2

Determine Information to Show Congruence

State the third congruence that must be given to prove that $\triangle ABC \cong \triangle PQR$ using the indicated postulate or theorem.

a. $\angle B \cong \angle Q$, $\angle C \cong \angle R$
   Use the ASA Congruence Postulate.

b. $\overline{BC} \cong \overline{QR}$, $\angle B \cong \angle Q$
   Use the SAS Congruence Postulate.

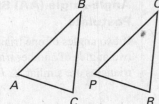

Solution

a. Two angles in the first triangle are congruent to two angles in the second triangle. To use the ASA Congruence Postulate, we need to know that the included side in the first triangle is congruent to the included side in the second triangle, or $\overline{BC} \cong \overline{QR}$.

c. One side and one angle in the first triangle are congruent to one side and one angle in the second triangle. To use the SAS Congruence Postulate, we need to know that another side of the first triangle is congruent to the corresponding side of the second triangle, such that the congruent angles are the included angles. So, $\overline{AB} \cong \overline{PQ}$.

Example 3

Determine Whether Triangles Are Congruent

Decide whether the congruence statement is true. Explain your reasoning.

a. $\triangle WYZ \cong \triangle YWX$

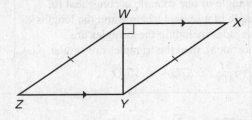

b. $\triangle VXY \cong \triangle ZXW$

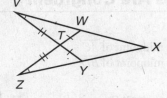

c. $\triangle JKL \cong \triangle MNO$

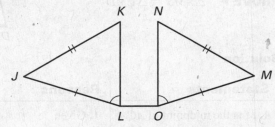

Solution

a. Yes, by the HL Congruence Theorem. $\angle WYZ$ is a right angle by the Corresponding Angles Postulate. $\overline{WY} \cong \overline{WY}$ by the Reflexive Property of Congruent Segments, and $\overline{ZW} \cong \overline{XY}$ is given.

b. Yes, by the AAS Congruence Theorem. $\angle X \cong \angle X$ by the Reflexive Property of Congruent Angles and $\angle V \cong \angle Z$ is given. $ZW = ZT + TW$ and $VY = VT + TY$ by the Segment Addition Postulate. $ZW = VY$ by the Transitive Property of Equality, and $\overline{ZW} \cong \overline{VY}$ by the Definition of Congruent Segments.

c. No; SSA is not one of the triangle congruence postulates or theorems.

Example 4

Use Corresponding Parts

Write a congruence statement for the triangles. Identify all pairs of congruent corresponding parts.

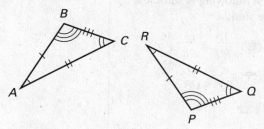

Solution

The diagram indicates that $\triangle ABC \cong \triangle RPQ$.

Corresponding angles $\angle A \cong \angle R, \angle B \cong \angle P, \angle C \cong \angle Q$

Corresponding sides $\overline{AB} \cong \overline{RP}, \overline{BC} \cong \overline{PQ}, \overline{CA} \cong \overline{QR}$

Example 5

Show Triangles Are Similar

Show that the triangles are similar and write a similarity statement. Explain your reasoning.

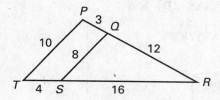

Solution

Since we know the lengths of the sides, calculate the ratios of corresponding sides.

$$\frac{QS}{PT} = \frac{8}{10} = \frac{4}{5} \qquad \frac{QR}{PR} = \frac{12}{3+12} = \frac{12}{15} = \frac{4}{5} \qquad \frac{SR}{TR} = \frac{16}{4+16} = \frac{16}{20} = \frac{4}{5}$$

$\frac{QS}{PT} = \frac{QR}{PR} = \frac{SR}{TR} = \frac{4}{5}$, thus the triangles are similar by the SSS Similarity Theorem.

Answer $\triangle TPR \sim \triangle SQR$ by the SSS Similarity Theorem.

Example 6

Prove Triangles Are Similar

GIVEN ▶ $\overline{KP} \cong \overline{LP}, JL = 21, KM = 14,$
$LQ = 24, NK = 16$

PROVE ▶ $\triangle JQL \sim \triangle MNK$

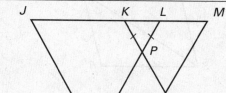

Solution

$\angle QLJ \cong \angle NKM$ by the Base Angles Theorem.

$$\frac{JL}{KM} = \frac{21}{14} = \frac{3}{2}$$

$$\frac{LQ}{NK} = \frac{24}{16} = \frac{3}{2}$$

The measures of the corresponding sides that include angles QLJ and NKM are proportional, so the triangles are similar by the SAS Similarity Theorem.

Name _____   Date _____

Exercises

California Standard Geometry 5.0

1. $\triangle JKL$ and $\triangle PQR$ are two triangles such that $\angle K \cong \angle Q$. Which of the following is sufficient to prove the triangles are similar?

(A) $JK = PQ$ **(B)** $\dfrac{JK}{PQ} = \dfrac{KL}{PR}$

(C) $\angle J$ is right.   **(D)** $\dfrac{JK}{PQ} = \dfrac{KL}{QR}$

2. In the figure below, $\overline{WZ} \parallel \overline{XY}$.

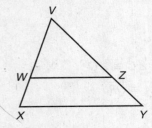

Which theorem or postulate can be used to prove $\triangle VWZ \sim \triangle VXY$?

(A) ASA   **(B)** AAS   **(C)** SAS   **(D)** SSS

3. In the figure below, $\triangle ABE \cong \triangle DCE$.

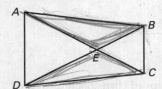

Which theorem or postulate can be used to prove $\triangle CDB \cong \triangle BAC$?

(A) ASA   **(B)** SSS   **(C)** SAS   **(D)** AAS

4. In the figure below, $\overline{PQ} \parallel \overline{SR}$.

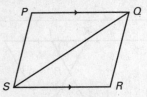

Which additional information would be enough to prove $\triangle PQS \cong \triangle RSQ$?

(A) $\overline{PQ} \cong \overline{PS}$ **(B)** $\overline{SR} \cong \overline{QR}$

(C) $\overline{PQ} \cong \overline{SR}$ **(D)** $\overline{PS} \cong \overline{QR}$

5. In the figure below, $\overline{HJ}$ bisects $\angle KHI$ and $\angle KJI$.

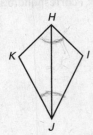

Which theorem or postulate can be used to prove $\triangle HKJ \cong \triangle HIJ$?

(A) ASA   **(B)** AAS

(C) SAS   **(D)** SSS

6. In the figure below, $\angle P \cong \angle X$.

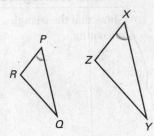

Which of the following would be sufficient to prove the triangles are similar?

(A) $\dfrac{RP}{ZX} = \dfrac{RQ}{XY}$ **(B)** $\dfrac{RP}{ZX} = \dfrac{PQ}{XY}$

(C) $\dfrac{RQ}{ZX} = \dfrac{RP}{ZY}$ **(D)** $\dfrac{RP}{ZX} = \dfrac{RQ}{ZY}$

7. In the figure below, $\overline{ED} \perp \overline{DF}$, $\overline{HG} \perp \overline{GF}$, F is the midpoint of $\overline{DG}$.

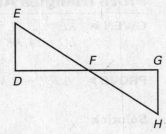

Which theorem or postulate can be used to prove $\triangle DEF \cong \triangle GHF$?

(A) ASA   **(B)** SSS   **(C)** SAS   **(D)** HL

Copyright © by McDougal Littell, a division of Houghton Mifflin Company.

California Standards Review and Practice
Geometry Standards

18

California Standards
Geometry 6.0

Students know and are able to use the triangle inequality theorem.

Triangle Inequality Theorem

Triangle Inequality Theorem	Example
The sum of the lengths of any two sides of a triangle is greater than the length of the third side.	$AB + BC > AC$ $AC + BC > AB$ $AB + AC > BC$

Example 1

Use the Triangle Inequality Theorem

Is it possible to construct a triangle with the given side lengths? If not, explain why not.

a. 3, 5, 7

b. 4, 6, 12

c. 19, 26, 35

Solution

a. $3 + 5 \overset{?}{>} 7$ $3 + 7 \overset{?}{>} 5$ $5 + 7 \overset{?}{>} 3$
     $8 > 7$ ✓ $10 > 5$ ✓ $12 > 3$ ✓
Yes, it is possible to construct a triangle with these side lengths.

b. $4 + 6 \overset{?}{>} 12$
     $10 < 12$ ✗
$4 + 6$ is not greater than 12. No, it is not possible to construct a triangle with these side lengths.

c. $19 + 26 \overset{?}{>} 35$ $19 + 35 \overset{?}{>} 26$ $26 + 35 \overset{?}{>} 19$
    $45 > 35$ ✓ $54 > 26$ ✓ $61 > 19$ ✓
Yes, it is possible to construct a triangle with these side lengths.

California Standard
Geometry 6.0

Example 2

Use the Triangle Inequality Theorem

A triangle has one side of length 17 and another of length 11. Describe the possible lengths of the third side.

Solution

Let x represent the length of the third side. Draw diagrams to help you visualize the possible lengths of the third side.

Small values of x	Large values of x

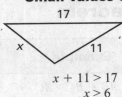 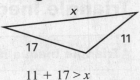

$$x + 11 > 17 \qquad\qquad 11 + 17 > x$$
$$x > 6 \qquad\qquad\qquad 28 > x, \text{ or } x < 28$$

Answer The length of the third side must be greater than 6 and less than 28.

Example 3

Use the Triangle Inequality Theorem

Describe the possible values of x.

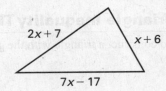

Solution

Check all three possible side length relationships.

$(x + 6) + (2x + 7) > 7x - 17 \qquad (2x + 7) + (7x - 17) > x + 6 \qquad (x + 6) + (7x - 17) > 2x + 7$

$\qquad 3x + 13 > 7x - 17 \qquad\qquad\qquad 9x - 10 > x + 6 \qquad\qquad\qquad 8x - 11 > 2x + 7$

$\qquad\qquad 30 > 4x \qquad\qquad\qquad\qquad\qquad 8x > 16 \qquad\qquad\qquad\qquad\qquad 6x > 18$

$\qquad\qquad 7\frac{1}{2} > x \qquad\qquad\qquad\qquad\qquad\quad x > 2 \qquad\qquad\qquad\qquad\qquad\quad x > 3$

Answer $3 < x < 7\frac{1}{2}$

Example 4

Use the Triangle Inequality Theorem

The triangle below is isosceles. If s is a whole number, what is its smallest possible value?

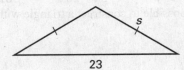

Solution

Use the Triangle Inequality Theorem to write and solve an inequality.

$$s + s > 23$$
$$2s > 23$$
$$s > 11\frac{1}{2}$$

The smallest whole number that is greater than $11\frac{1}{2}$ is 12.

Answer The smallest possible value for s is 12.

Exercises

1. Two sides of a triangle measure 14 and 9. Which of the following cannot be the perimeter of the triangle?

(A) 28 (B) 37

(C) 42 (D) 46

2. The lengths of two sides of the triangle are known.

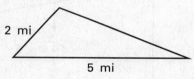

Which of the following could be the perimeter of the triangle?

(A) 19 (B) 24

(C) 31 (D) 38

3. The figure shows the route Daniel took while riding his bicycle after school.

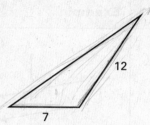

Which of the following is *not* a possible measure for the third side of the triangle?

(A) 4 mi (B) 5 mi

(C) 6 mi (D) 7 mi

4. The figure shows the outline of a flower garden.

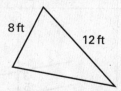

Which of the following is a possible measure for the third side of the garden?

(A) 4 ft (B) 8 ft

(C) 20 ft (D) 24 ft

5. The triangle below is isosceles.

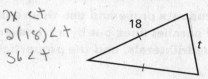

$x < t$
$2(18) < t$
$36 < t$

If *t* is a whole number, what is its largest possible value?

(A) 35 (B) 36 (C) 37 (D) 38

6. A triangle has one side of length 12 and another of length 19. Which of the following best describes the possible lengths of the third side?

(A) $7 < x < 31$

(B) $12 < x < 31$

(C) $7 < x < 19$

(D) $12 < x < 19$

7. Which of the following sets of numbers could *not* represent the lengths of the sides of a triangle?

(A) 3, 4, 6 (B) 2, 4, 7

(C) 5, 5, 8 (D) 4, 7, 10

8. Which of the following figures could represent a real triangle?

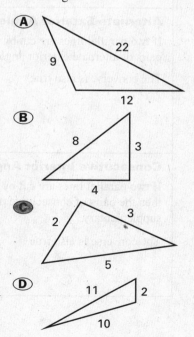

California Standards
Geometry 7.0

Students prove and use theorems involving the properties of parallel lines cut by a transversal, the properties of quadrilaterals, and the properties of circles.

Parallel Lines, Quadrilaterals, and Circles

Parallel Lines and Transversals	Example
Corresponding Angles Postulate If two parallel lines are cut by a transversal, then the pairs of corresponding angles are congruent. The converse is also true.	 $\angle 2 \cong \angle 6$
Alternate Interior Angles Theorem If two parallel lines are cut by a transversal, then the pairs of alternate interior angles are congruent. The converse is also true.	 $\angle 4 \cong \angle 5$
Alternate Exterior Angles Theorem If two parallel lines are cut by a transversal, then the pairs of alternate exterior angles are congruent. The converse is also true.	 $\angle 1 \cong \angle 8$
Consecutive Interior Angles Theorem If two parallel lines are cut by a transversal, then the pairs of consecutive interior angles are supplementary. The converse is also true.	 $\angle 3$ and $\angle 5$ are supplementary.

California Standard
Geometry 7.0

Parallelograms	Example
If a quadrilateral is a parallelogram, then its opposite sides are congruent. The converse is also true.	
If a quadrilateral is a parallelogram, then its opposite angles are congruent. The converse is also true.	
If a quadrilateral is a parallelogram, then its consecutive angles are supplementary. If $PQRS$ is a parallelogram, then $x° + y° = 180°$.	
If a quadrilateral is a parallelogram, then its diagonals bisect each other. The converse is also true.	
If one pair of opposite sides of a quadrilateral are congruent and parallel, then the quadrilateral is a parallelogram.	

Special Parallelograms	Example	Special Parallelograms	Example
A quadrilateral is a rhombus if and only if it has four congruent sides.		A parallelogram is a rhombus if and only if its diagonals are perpendicular.	
A quadrilateral is a rectangle if and only if it has four right angles.		A parallelogram is a rhombus if and only if each diagonal bisects a pair of opposite angles.	
A quadrilateral is a square if and only if it is a rhombus and a rectangle.		A parallelogram is a rectangle if and only if its diagonals are congruent.	

California Standard
Geometry 7.0

Trapezoids and Kites	Example
If a trapezoid is isosceles, then each pair of base angles is congruent.	
If a trapezoid has a pair of congruent base angles, then it is an isosceles trapezoid.	
A trapezoid is isosceles if and only if its diagonals are congruent.	$\overline{AC} \cong \overline{BD}$

Trapezoids and Kites	Example
The midsegment of a trapezoid is parallel to each base, and its length is one half the sum of the lengths of the bases.	$MN = \frac{1}{2}(AD + BC)$
If a quadrilateral is a kite, then its diagonals are perpendicular.	
If a quadrilateral is a kite, then exactly one pair of opposite angles are congruent.	

Circles	Example
A **circle** is the set of all points in a plane that are equidistant from a given point called the **center** of the circle. A **radius** is a segment whose endpoints are the center and any point on the circle. A **chord** is a segment whose endpoints are on a circle. A **diameter** is a chord that contains the center of the circle.	radius center diameter chord
A **central angle** of a circle is an angle whose vertex is the center of the circle. In the diagram, $\angle ACB$ is a central angle of circle C. If $m\angle ACB < 180°$, then the points on circle C that lie in the interior of $\angle ACB$ form a **minor arc** with endpoints A and B. The points on circle C that do not lie on minor arc $\overset{\frown}{AB}$ form a **major arc** with endpoints A and B. A **semicircle** is an arc with endpoints that are the endpoints of a diameter.	minor arc $\overset{\frown}{AB}$ major arc $\overset{\frown}{ADB}$
The **measure of a minor arc** is the measure of its central angle. The expression $m\overset{\frown}{AB}$ is read as "the measure of arc AB." The measure of the entire circle is 360°. The **measure of a major arc** is the difference between 360° and the measure of the related minor arc. The measure of a semicircle is 180°.	$m\overset{\frown}{AB} = 60°$ $m\overset{\frown}{ADB} = 360° - 60° = 300°$

Example 1   ## Parallel Lines and Transversals

Find $m\angle 1$ and $m\angle 2$. Explain your reasoning.

Solution

$\angle 2$ and the given angle are alternate exterior angles. So, $\angle 2$ is congruent to the given angle by the Alternate Exterior Angles Theorem. Therefore, $m\angle 2 = 110°$.

Since $\angle 1$ and $\angle 2$ form a linear pair, they are supplementary angles. So,
$m\angle 1 = 180° - m\angle 2 = 180° - 110° = 70°$.

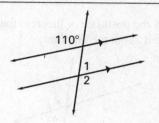

Example 2   ## Prove That Figures Are Congruent

Write a proof.

GIVEN ▶ kite $FGHI$ with diagonal $\overline{GI}$

PROVE ▶ $\triangle IFG \cong \triangle IHG$

Solution

Because $FGHI$ is a kite, $\overline{FG} \cong \overline{HG}$ and $\overline{FI} \cong \overline{HI}$.

By the Reflexive Property, $\overline{GI} \cong \overline{GI}$.

So, $\triangle IFG \cong \triangle IHG$ by the SSS Congruence Postulate.

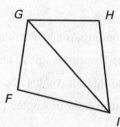

Example 3   ## Find Measures of Arcs

$\overline{AC}$ is a diameter of circle E. Identify the given arc as a *major arc*, *minor arc*, or *semicircle*, and find the measure of the arc.

a. $\overset{\frown}{AD}$ **b.** $\overset{\frown}{DBC}$

c. $\overset{\frown}{ABC}$ **d.** $\overset{\frown}{BC}$

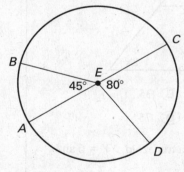

Solution

a. $m\overset{\frown}{AD} = m\overset{\frown}{ADC} - m\overset{\frown}{DC}$

  $= 180° - 80°$

  $= 100°$

  $m\overset{\frown}{AD}$ is less than 180°. It is a minor arc.

c. $\overline{AC}$ is a diameter.

  $m\overset{\frown}{ABC}$ is 180°. It is semicircle.

b. $m\overset{\frown}{DBC} = 360° - m\overset{\frown}{DC}$

  $= 360° - 80°$

  $= 280°$

  $m\overset{\frown}{DBC}$ is more than 180°. It is a major arc.

d. $m\overset{\frown}{BC} = m\overset{\frown}{ABC} - m\overset{\frown}{AB}$

  $= 180° - 45°$

  $= 135°$

  $m\overset{\frown}{BC}$ is less than 180°. It is a minor arc.

Exercises

1. Identify the postulate or theorem that justifies the statement about the diagram.

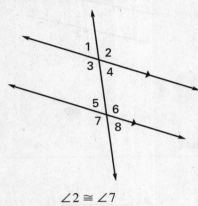

$$\angle 2 \cong \angle 7$$

- (A) Corresponding Angles Postulate
- (B) Alternate Exterior Angles Theorem
- (C) Alternate Interior Angles Theorem
- (D) Consecutive Interior Angles Theorem

2. What is the value of x in the diagram?

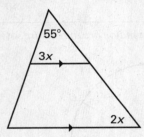

- (A) 25°
- (B) 35°
- (C) 45°
- (D) 75°

3. Quadrilateral *WXYZ* is a trapezoid. $XY = 6$ and $WZ = 10$. What is *MN*?

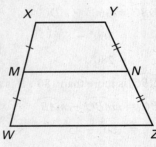

- (A) 3
- (B) 6
- (C) 8
- (D) 10

4. Quadrilateral *JKLM* is a parallelogram. If its diagonals are perpendicular, which statement must be true?

- (A) Quadrilateral *JKLM* is a rectangle.
- (B) Quadrilateral *JKLM* is a rhombus.
- (C) Quadrilateral *JKLM* is an isosceles trapezoid.
- (D) Quadrilateral *JKLM* is a square.

5. $\overline{GH}$ and $\overline{JK}$ are diameters of circle *C*. If $m\widehat{HK} = 35°$, what is $m\widehat{GJK}$?

- (A) 55°
- (B) 145°
- (C) 215°
- (D) 325°

6. In the figure below, *PQRS* is a parallelogram.

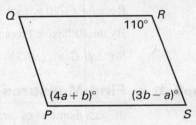

What are the values of a and b?

- (A) $a = 70, b = 110$
- (B) $a = 110, b = 70$
- (C) $a = 30, b = 20$
- (D) $a = 20, b = 30$

7. In the figure below, circle *M* has a diameter of 8 and $m\widehat{PQ} = 90°$.

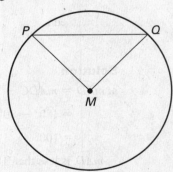

What is the length of $\overline{PQ}$?

- (A) 4
- (B) $4\sqrt{2}$
- (C) 8
- (D) $8\sqrt{2}$

California Standards
Geometry 8.0

Students know, derive, and solve problems involving perimeter, circumference, area, volume, lateral area, and surface area of common geometric figures.

Perimeter, Area, and Volume

Terms to Know	Example
The **perimeter** of a figure is the distance around it.	$P = 4s$ $P = 2\ell + 2w$ $P = a + b + c$
Circumference is the distance around a circle.	$C = \pi d = 2\pi r$
Area is the amount of surface covered by a figure.	$A = \ell w$ $A = \frac{1}{2}bh$ $A = \pi r^2$
The **volume** of a solid is the number of cubic units contained in its interior.	$V = Bh = \ell wh$
A face of a solid that is not a base is a **lateral face.** The **lateral area** of a solid is the sum of the areas of its lateral faces.	$L = 2h\ell + 2hw$
The **surface area** of a solid is the sum of the areas of all of its faces.	$S = 2h\ell + 2hw + 2\ell w$

Example 1

Find the Unknown Length

The perimeter of the triangle is 17.25 feet. Find the length of b.

Solution

$$P = a + b + c$$

$17.25 = 5 + 6.5 + b$

$17.25 = 11.5 + b$

$5.75 = b$

Answer   The length of b is 5.75 feet.

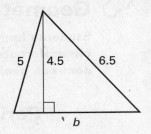

Example 2

Find the Circumference

A circular stained-glass window has a diameter of 80 centimeters. Find the approximate circumference of the window. Use 3.14 for π.

Solution

$C = \pi d$

$C = 3.14(80) = 251.2$

Answer   The circumference of the window is approximately 251.2 centimeters.

Example 3

Find the Area

In the diagram, the diameter of the large circle is three times the diameter of the small circle. What fraction of the large circle is covered by the shaded region?

Solution

Small circle: $A = \pi r^2 = \pi x^2$

Large circle: $A = \pi r^2 = \pi(3x)^2 = 9\pi x^2$

Shaded region: $A = 9\pi x^2 - \pi x^2 = 8\pi x^2$

$$\frac{\text{Area of shaded region}}{\text{Area of large circle}} = \frac{8\pi x^2}{9\pi x^2} = \frac{8}{9}$$

Answer   The shaded region covers $\frac{8}{9}$ of the large circle.

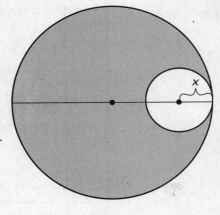

Example 4

Find the Lateral Area

The lateral area of the cylinder is 376.8 square inches. Find the height of the cylinder. Use 3.14 for π. (The lateral area of a right cylinder is $2\pi rh$, where h is the height of the cylinder.)

Solution

$L = 2\pi rh$

$376.8 = 2(3.14)(4)h$

$376.8 = (25.12)h$

$h = 15$

Answer   The height of the cylinder is 15 inches.

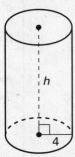

Example 5

Find the Surface Area

Krista is making a cardboard box for a science project. How many square centimeters of cardboard does she need?

Solution

$A = 2h\ell + 2hw + 2\ell w$

$= 2(8)(10) + 2(8)(20) + 2(10)(20)$

$= 160 + 320 + 400$

$= 880$

Answer Krista will need 880 cm^2 of cardboard.

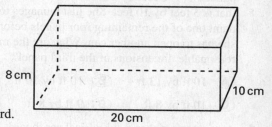

8 cm

10 cm

20 cm

Example 6

Find the Volume

Find the volume of the solid in the diagram.

Solution

V = volume of outer prism − volume of hole

$= 40(40)(15) − 20(30)(15)$

$= 24{,}000 − 9000$

$= 15{,}000$

Answer The volume of the solid is 15,000 mm^3.

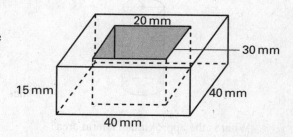

20 mm

30 mm

15 mm

40 mm

40 mm

Exercises

1. What is the perimeter of quadrilateral *RSTU* shown below?

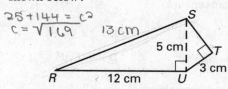

$25 + 144 = c^2$
$c = \sqrt{169}$ 13 cm

S

5 cm

T

3 cm

R   12 cm   U

(A) 20 cm   (B) 30 cm

● 32 cm   (D) 37 cm

2. Mrs. Taylor wants to paint the walls of her rectangular office. She knows the width w, length ℓ, and height h of the office, and the cost per square foot of paint. Which of the following expressions should she use to determine the area she must paint?

(A) $(2\ell + 2w)h$ (B) $2(\ell + w + h)$

(C) $\frac{1}{2}(\ell + w)h$ ● $\ell w h$

3. A farmer has planted corn and akra on the piece of land shown below.

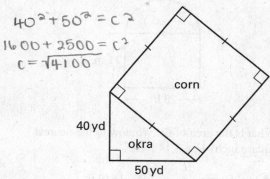

$40^2 + 50^2 = c^2$
$1600 + 2500 = c^2$
$c = \sqrt{4100}$

corn

40 yd

okra

50 yd

What is the area of the section planted with corn?

(A) 2000 yd^2 (B) 4000 yd^2

● 4100 yd^2 (D) 4600 yd^2

4. A 10-ounce rectangular box of cereal has dimensions 10.5 inches by 7.5 inches by 2.5 inches. What is the approximate volume?

(A) 123.8 in.^{3} (B) 196.9 in.^{3}

(C) 247.4 in.^{3} (D) 393.8 in.^{3}

5. Justine is painting rectangular panels in a restaurant. She is using a can of enamel that covers at most 200 square feet. She has painted a panel that is 8 feet by 8 feet and a second panel that is 3 feet by 10 feet. She just manages to paint one of the remaining four panels before she has to open another can. What are the most reasonable dimensions of the third panel?

Ⓐ 10 ft by 13 ft Ⓑ 10 ft by 10 ft

Ⓒ 10 ft by 8 ft Ⓓ 9 ft by 8 ft

6. A company makes a cylindrical cardboard container with the dimensions shown below.

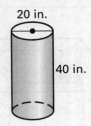

20 in.

40 in.

What is the approximate lateral area?

Ⓐ 1257 in.² Ⓑ 2513 in.²

Ⓒ 5027 in.² Ⓓ 12,566 in.²

7. An architect designed a window with the dimensions shown below.

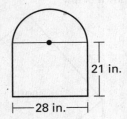

21 in.

28 in.

What is the area of the window to the nearest square inch? Use 3.14 for π.

Ⓐ 3050 in.² Ⓑ 1819 in.²

Ⓒ 1203 in.² Ⓓ 896 in.²

8. Ava made a pencil holder in the shape of an open square prism that has a volume of 96 cubic inches. If the sides of the base are 4 inches long, what is the height?

Ⓐ 4 in. Ⓑ 6 in.

Ⓒ 8 in. Ⓓ 24 in.

9. Joshua has tied his horse's rope to a post in a pasture so that the horse can eat some grass. The portion of the rope between the horse and the post is 12 feet long. To the nearest whole number, what is the area of the circular region of the pasture where the horse will be able to graze?

Ⓐ 452 ft² Ⓑ 144 ft²

Ⓒ 75 ft² Ⓓ 38 ft²

10. Eli has roped off a square inside his circular pool so that he and his friends can play a game.

3 yd

To the nearest tenth, what is the area of the pool's surface that is *not* contained within the roped-off square region?

Ⓐ 18.8 yd² Ⓑ 14.3 yd²

Ⓒ 10.3 yd² Ⓓ 9.0 yd²

11. What is the volume of this solid?

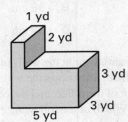

1 yd
2 yd
3 yd
3 yd
5 yd

Ⓐ 14 yd³ Ⓑ 51 yd³

Ⓒ 169 yd³ Ⓓ 270 yd³

California Standard
Geometry 8.0

California Standards
Geometry 9.0

Students compute the volumes and surface areas of prisms, pyramids, cylinders, cones, and spheres; and students commit to memory the formulas for prisms, pyramids, and cylinders.

Volume and Surface Area

Terms to Know	Example
A **prism** is a polyhedron with two bases that are congruent polygons in parallel planes. In a **right prism,** each lateral edge is perpendicular to both bases. A prism with lateral edges that are not perpendicular to the bases is an **oblique prism.**	triangular prism pentagonal prism (apothem)
A **pyramid** is a polyhedron with a polygon for its base. All of the other faces intersect at one vertex. A **regular pyramid** has a regular polygon for a base, and the segment joining the vertex and the center of the base is perpendicular to the base.	triangular pyramid rectangular pyramid (height, slant height)
A **cylinder** is a solid with congruent circular bases that lie in parallel planes. In a **right cylinder,** the segment joining the centers of the bases is perpendicular to the bases. In an **oblique cylinder,** the segment joining the centers of the bases is *not* perpendicular to the bases.	cylinder right cylinder (height)
A **cone** has a circular base and a vertex that is not in the same plane as the base. In a **right cone,** the segment joining the vertex and the center of the base is perpendicular to the base.	cone right cone (height, slant height)
A **sphere** is the set of all points in space equidistant from a given point, called the center.	sphere (center, radius)

Solid	Volume	Surface Area
prism B is the area of a base, h is the height, a is the apothem of a base, and P is the perimeter of a base.	$V = Bh$	$S = 2B + Ph = aP + Ph$ (right prism)
pyramid B is the area of the base, h is the height, P is the perimeter of the base, and ℓ is the slant height.	$V = \frac{1}{3}Bh$	$S = B + \frac{1}{2}P\ell$ (regular pyramid)
cylinder B is the area of a base, h is the height, r is the radius of a base, C is the circumference of a base, and h is the height.	$V = Bh = \pi r^2 h$	$S = 2B + Ch = 2\pi r^2 + 2\pi rh$
cone B is the area of the base, h is the height, r is the radius of the base, C is the circumference of the base, and ℓ is the slant height.	$V = \frac{1}{3}Bh = \frac{1}{3}\pi r^2 h$	$S = B + \frac{1}{2}CL = \pi r^2 + \pi r\ell$ (right cone)
sphere r is the radius.	$V = \frac{4}{3}\pi r^3$	$S = 4\pi r^2$

Example 1

Find the Volume of a Prism

Find the volume of the right prism.

Solution

Find the area of the base. $B = \frac{1}{2}h(b_1 + b_2) = \frac{1}{2}(6)(4 + 11) = 45$

[Note: h in this area formula is the height of the trapezoid, *not* the height of the prism.]

Find the volume.　　　$V = Bh = (45)(2) = 90$

Answer The volume of the prism is 90 ft^3.

Example 2

Find the Volume of a Pyramid

Find the volume of the pyramid.

Solution

Find the area of the base.　　$B = \frac{1}{2}bh = \frac{1}{2}(9)(7) = 31.5$

[Note: h in this area formula is the height of the triangle, *not* the height of the pyramid.]

Find the volume.　　$V = \frac{1}{3}Bh = \frac{1}{3}(31.5)(8) = 84$

Answer The volume of the pyramid is 84 m^3.

Example 3

Find the Volume of a Sphere

Find the volume of the sphere. Use 3.14 for π.

Solution

The diameter is given. Find the radius. $r = \dfrac{d}{2} = \dfrac{14}{2} = 7$

$V = \dfrac{4}{3}\pi r^3 = \dfrac{4}{3}(3.14)(7^3) \approx 1436$

Answer The volume of the sphere is approximately 1436 cm³.

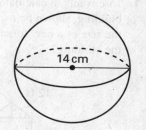

Example 4

Find the Surface Area of a Cylinder

Find the surface area of the cylinder. Use 3.14 for π.

Solution

The diameter is given. Find the radius. $r = \dfrac{d}{2} = \dfrac{40}{2} = 20$

Find the surface area.

$S = 2\pi r^2 + 2\pi rh = 2(3.14)(20^2) + 2(3.14)(20)(16) \approx 4522$

Answer The surface area of the cylinder is approximately 4522 ft².

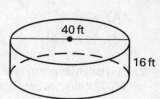

Example 5

Find the Surface Area of a Cone

Find the surface area of the cone. Use 3.14 for π.

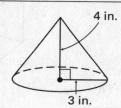

Solution

Find the slant height. $\ell^2 = 4^2 + 3^2$

$\ell = \sqrt{16 + 9} = \sqrt{25} = 5$

Find the surface area. $S = \pi r^2 + \pi r\ell = 3.14(3^2) + 3.14(3)(5) \approx 75$

Answer The surface area of the cone is approximately 75 in.².

Example 6

Find the Surface Area of a Sphere

Find the surface area of the sphere. Use 3.14 for π.

Solution

$S = 4\pi r^2 = 4(3.14)(12^2) \approx 1809$

Answer The surface area of the sphere is approximately
1809 mm².

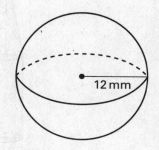

Exercises

1. Jose wants to calculate the volume of air in a building, shown below, so that he can decide on the size of a new furnace. What is the volume of the building?

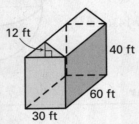

12 ft
40 ft
60 ft
30 ft

(A) 8280 ft³

(B) 82,800 ft³

(C) 72,000 ft³

(D) 93,600 ft³

2. A triangular prism is shown below. Its volume is 672 cubic inches. What is the height x of the prism?

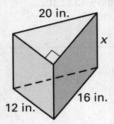

20 in.
x
16 in.
12 in.

(A) 7 in.

(B) 10 in.

(C) 12 in.

(D) 17.1 in.

3. The diagram represents a sculpture in an art museum. What is the surface area of the sculpture? Round your answer to the nearest tenth. Use 3.14 for π.

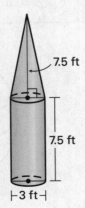

7.5 ft
7.5 ft
├3 ft┤

(A) 113.8 ft²

(B) 127.9 ft²

(C) 241.7 ft²

(D) 301.8 ft²

4. Which of the following is the approximate volume of a ball that has a diameter of 9 inches? Use 3.14 for π.

(A) 85 in.³

(B) 286 in.³

(C) 339 in.³

(D) 382 in.³

5. The manufacturer of a concentrated floor cleaning solution recommends that it be diluted so that the final mixture is 1 part cleaning solution to 8 parts water. Mia pours 120 cubic inches of water into the cylindrical bucket shown below and then adds the correct amount of cleaning solution.

12 in.
├ 10 in. ┤

Which expression represents how many more cubic inches of liquid the bucket can hold?

(A) $\pi \cdot 5^2 \cdot 12 - \left(120 + \frac{1}{8} \cdot 120\right)$

(B) $\pi \cdot 5^2 \cdot 12 + 120 + \cdot 120$

(C) $\pi \cdot 10^2 \cdot 12 - \left(120 + \frac{1}{8} \cdot 120\right)$

(D) $\pi \cdot 10^2 \cdot 12 - 8 \cdot 120$

6. What is the approximate volume of the paper water cup shown below? Use 3.14 for π.

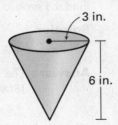

3 in.
6 in.

(A) 56.5 in.³

(B) 108 in.³

(C) 113.1 in.³

(D) 226.2 in.³

7. The top of the grain silo shown below is a hemisphere. What is the approximate volume of the silo? Use 3.14 for π.

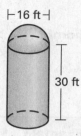

⊢16 ft⊣

30 ft

Ⓐ 1910 ft³   Ⓑ 2111 ft³

Ⓒ 2312 ft³   Ⓓ 7101 ft³

8. A basketball with circumference 78 centimeters touches all six sides of its cubical shipping box. Approximately what percent of the space inside the box is *not* occupied by the basketball? Use 3.14 for π.

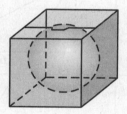

Ⓐ 15%   Ⓑ 25%

Ⓒ 48%   Ⓓ 75%

9. Naomi has built part of a sandcastle in the shape of a cone with the dimensions shown. To the nearest cubic inch, what is the volume of this cone? Use 3.14 for π.

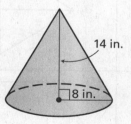

14 in.

8 in.

Ⓐ 1407 in.³   Ⓑ 1081 in.³

Ⓒ 938 in.³   Ⓓ 299 in.³

10. A three-quarter circle with radius 8 inches is made into a hat by attaching the edges of the cutout. What is the best estimate for the height of the hat if the diameter of the base is 12 inches?

Ⓐ 5.3 in. Ⓑ 8 in.   Ⓒ 8.9 in. Ⓓ 10 in.

11. A cylindrical salt shaker has a radius of 20 millimeters and a height of 90 millimeters. What is the volume of the salt shaker? Round your answer to the nearest cubic millimeter. Use 3.14 for π.

Ⓐ 113,040 mm³   Ⓑ 62,424 mm³

Ⓒ 28,274 mm³   Ⓓ 13,823 mm³

12. The dome of a building is a hemisphere with a diameter of 50 feet. What is the surface area of the dome, rounded to the nearest square foot? Use 3.14 for π.

Ⓐ 1571 ft²   Ⓑ 3925 ft²

Ⓒ 7854 ft²   Ⓓ 32,725 ft²

13. The pyramid below is a representation of a trellis for Marla's flowering vine. The base is a regular hexagon. What is the surface area of the pyramid, including the base? Round your answer to the nearest hundredth.

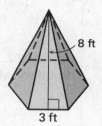

8 ft

3 ft

Ⓐ 23.38 ft²   Ⓑ 72.00 ft²

Ⓒ 95.38 ft²   Ⓓ 167.38 ft²

14. Archie built a ramp using one rectangular piece of wood for the top and two triangular pieces for the sides, as shown below. To the nearest tenth of a square foot, what is the total surface area of the plywood Archie used to build the ramp?

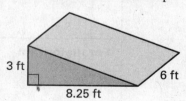

3 ft

6 ft

8.25 ft

Ⓐ 44.9 ft²   Ⓑ 52.7 ft²

Ⓒ 65.0 ft²   Ⓓ 77.4 ft²

California Standard Geometry 9.0

California Standards
Geometry 10.0

Students compute areas of polygons, including rectangles, scalene triangles, equilateral triangles, rhombi, parallelograms, and trapezoids.

Area

Polygon	Area Formula	Example
Rectangle	$A = bh$ b is the base. h is the height.	
Triangle	$A = \frac{1}{2}bh$ b is the base. h is the height.	
Equilateral Triangle	$A = \frac{\sqrt{3}s^2}{4}$ s is a side.	
Rhombus	$A = \frac{1}{2}d_1 d_2$ d_1 and d_2 are the diagonals.	
Parallelogram	$A = bh$ b is the base. h is the height.	
Trapezoid	$A = \frac{1}{2}h(b_1 + b_2)$ b_1 and b_2 are the bases. h is the height.	

Example 1 Area of a Rectangle

The area of a rectangular field is 4675 square feet. The field is 55 feet wide. Find the length of the field.

Solution

Let b be the length and h be the width of the field.

$A = bh$	**Formula for area of a rectangle**
$4675 = b(55)$	**Substitute 4675 for A and 55 for h.**
$b = 85$	**Simplify.**

Answer The length of the field is 85 feet.

Example 2 Area of a Triangle

The base of a triangle is three times its height. The area of the triangle is 96 square meters. Find the base and height of the triangle.

Solution

Let h represent the height of the triangle. Then the base is $3h$.

$A = \frac{1}{2}bh$	**Formula for area of a triangle**
$96 = \frac{1}{2}(3h)(h)$	**Substitute 96 for A and $3h$ for b.**
$96 = \frac{3}{2}h^2$	**Simplify.**
$64 = h^2$	**Multiply each side by $\frac{2}{3}$.**
$8 = h$	**Find the positive square root of each side.**

Answer The height of the triangle is 8 meters, and the base is 24 meters.

Example 3 Area of an Equilateral Triangle

An equilateral triangle has a side length of 12 centimeters. What is the area of the triangle?

Solution

$$A = \frac{\sqrt{3}s^2}{4} = \frac{\sqrt{3}(12)^2}{4} = 36\sqrt{3} \approx 62.4$$

Answer The area of the triangle is about 62.4 square centimeters.

Example 4 Area of a Rhombus

Rhombus $ABCD$ has an area of 98 square meters. Find AC if $BD = 7$ meters.

Solution

$A = \frac{1}{2}d_1 d_2$	**Formula for area of a rhombus**
$98 = \frac{1}{2}(7)d_2$	**Substitute 49 for A and 7 for d_1.**
$28 = d_2$	**Simplify.**

Answer AC equals 28 meters.

Example 5 ## Area of a Parallelogram

A cornfield is shaped like a parallelogram. Find the area of the field in acres. There are 4840 square yards in one acre.

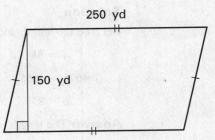

250 yd

150 yd

Solution

Find the area of the field in square yards.

$$A = bh = (250)(150) = 37,500 \text{ yd}^2$$

Change the units to acres.

$$37,500 \text{ yd}^2 \cdot \frac{1 \text{ acre}}{4840 \text{ yd}^2} \approx 7.75 \text{ acres}$$ **Use unit analysis.**

Answer The area of the field is about 7.75 acres.

Example 6 ## Area of a Trapezoid

The Art Club needs to buy primer paint so that members can prime one wall of the school before painting a new mural. A gallon of primer paint covers 300 square feet. How many gallons of primer paint should the club buy?

32 ft

28 ft

40 ft

Solution

Find the area of the wall.

$$A = \frac{1}{2}h(b_1 + b_2) = \frac{1}{2}(28)(32 + 40) = \frac{1}{2}(28)(72)$$
$$= 1008 \text{ ft}^2$$

Determine how many gallons of primer paint are needed.

$$1008 \text{ ft}^2 \cdot \frac{1 \text{ gal}}{300 \text{ ft}^2} = 3.36 \text{ gal}$$ **Use unit analysis.**

Answer Round up so there is enough primer paint. The Art Club should buy 4 gallons of primer paint.

Exercises

1. Dan and Marie built a deck behind their house. A sketch of the deck's floor is shown below. They are planning to waterproof the top of the deck and need to find its area so they know how many gallons of water sealant to buy. If one gallon of water sealant covers 150 square feet, how many gallons of water sealant are required for the deck? Round your answer to the nearest tenth.

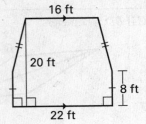

16 ft

20 ft

8 ft

22 ft

(A) 2.7 gal   (B) 2.9 gal

(C) 3.7 gal   (D) 4.0 gal

2. In isosceles trapezoid $ABCD$, $AB = 28$ inches and $DC = 48$ inches. What additional data does *not* provide sufficient information to find the area of the trapezoid?

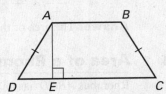

A   B

D   E   C

(A) the perimeter of the trapezoid

(B) the length of $\overline{BC}$

(C) the measure of $\angle AED$

(D) the length of $\overline{AE}$

3. Chase has a clock in his room with a clock face in the shape of an equilateral triangle. The area of the clock face is $16\sqrt{3}$ square inches. What is the length of a side of the clock face?

(A) 4 in. (B) 6 in. (C) 8 in. (D) 10 in.

4. Brett is using wallpaper to decorate two walls of his bedroom. Each wall is 14 feet by 18 feet. If one roll covers about 27 square feet, how many rolls will Brett need to cover both walls?

(A) 9 rolls   (B) 10 rolls
(C) 18 rolls   (D) 19 rolls

5. What is the area of the triangle below?

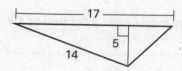

(A) 35 units²   (B) 42.5 units²
(C) 70 units²   (D) 85 units²

6. The figure below is a square with four congruent rhombi inside.

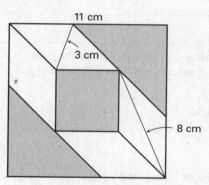

What is the area of the shaded portion?

(A) 25 cm²   (B) 48 cm²
(C) 73 cm²   (D) 109 cm²

7. What is the area of the quadrilateral below?

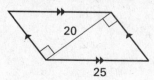

(A) 150 units²   (B) 200 units²
(C) 250 units²   (D) 300 units²

8. What is the area of the parallelogram shown below?

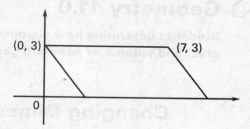

(A) 10 units²   (B) 10.5 units²
(C) 20 units²   (D) 21 units²

9. The height of a triangle is 1.5 times the length of its base. The area of the triangle is 75 square feet. What is the height of the triangle?

(A) 10 ft   (B) 15 ft
(C) $5\sqrt{2}$ ft   (D) $10\sqrt{2}$ ft

10. The quadrilateral shown below is a rhombus. What is the area of $\triangle QRS$?

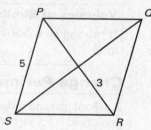

(A) 6 units²   (B) 12 units²
(C) 24 units²   (D) 48 units²

11. In isosceles triangle JKL, $JK = 8$ centimeters. What additional data does *not* provide sufficient information to find the area of the triangle?

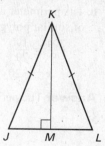

(A) the perimeter of the triangle
(B) the length of $\overline{KM}$
(C) the measure of $\angle JKL$
(D) the length of $\overline{KL}$

California Standard
Geometry 11.0

California Standard

Geometry 11.0

Students determine how changes in dimensions affect the perimeter, area, and volume of common geometric figures and solids.

Changing Dimensions

Theorem
Perimeters of Similar Polygons
If two polygons are similar, then the ratio of their perimeters is equal to the ratios of their corresponding side lengths.
Areas of Similar Polygons
If two polygons are similar with the lengths of corresponding sides in the ratio of $a:b$, then the ratio of their areas is $a^2:b^2$.
Surface Areas of Similar Solids
If two similar solids have a scale factor of $a:b$, then corresponding areas have a ratio of $a^2:b^2$.
Volumes of Similar Solids
If two similar solids have a scale factor of $a:b$, then corresponding volumes have a ratio of $a^3:b^3$.

Example 1

Change Perimeter

A school plans to install a synthetic-turf field to replace a grass one. The rectangular grass field is 95 yards long and 57 yards wide. The synthetic-turf field will be similar in shape, but it will be 60 yards wide.

a. Find the scale factor of the old field to the new field.

b. Find the perimeter of the new field.

Solution

a. The scale factor of the old field to the new field is the ratio of the widths, $\frac{57}{60} = \frac{19}{20}$.

b. The perimeter of the original field is $2(57) + 2(95) = 304$ yards. Use the perimeter of similar polygons theorem to find the perimeter x of the new field.

$$\frac{304}{x} = \frac{19}{20} \qquad \textbf{Write a proportion.}$$

$$x = 320 \qquad \textbf{Cross multiply and simplify.}$$

Answer The perimeter of the new field is 320 yards.

Example 2

Change Area

A large rectangular tabletop is 64 inches long by
36 inches wide. A smaller tabletop is similar to the large
tabletop. The area of the smaller tabletop is 1296 square
inches. Find the width of the smaller tabletop.

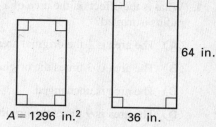

$A = 1296$ in.²   36 in.   64 in.

Solution

If the area ratio is $a^2 : b^2$, then the length ratio is $a : b$.

$$\frac{\text{Area of smaller tabletop}}{\text{Area of larger tabletop}} = \frac{1296}{2304} = \frac{9}{16}$$ **Write the ratio of known areas. Then simplify.**

$$\frac{\text{Length of smaller tabletop}}{\text{Length of larger tabletop}} = \frac{\sqrt{9}}{\sqrt{16}} = \frac{3}{4}$$ **Find the square root of the area ratio.**

Any length in the smaller tabletop is $\frac{3}{4}$, or 0.75, of the corresponding length in the
larger tabletop. So, the width of the smaller tabletop is 0.75(36 inches) = 27 inches.

Answer The width of the smaller tabletop is 27 inches.

Example 3

Change Surface Area

The coffee filters shown are similar with a scale factor of 77 : 100. Find the surface
area of the larger coffee filter.

Solution

Write a proportion.

$$\frac{\text{Surface area of I}}{\text{Surface area of II}} = \frac{a^2}{b^2}$$

$$\frac{47.12}{\text{Surface area of II}} = \frac{77^2}{100^2}$$

Surface area of II = 79.47

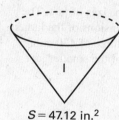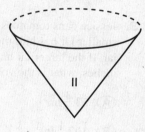

I   II

$S = 47.12$ in.²

Answer The surface area of the larger coffee filter is about 79.47 square inches.

Example 4

Change Volume

The prisms shown are similar with a scale factor of 2 : 3.
Find the volume of the larger prism.

Solution

If the two similar solids have a scale
factor of $a : b$, then the corresponding
volumes have a ratio of $a^3 : b^3$.

$$\frac{\text{Volume of smaller prism}}{\text{Volume of larger prism}} = \frac{a^3}{b^3}$$

$$\frac{16}{\text{Volume of larger prism}} = \frac{2^3}{3^3}$$

Volume of larger prism = 54

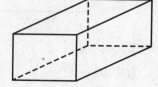

$V = 16$ in.³

Answer The volume of the larger prism is 54 cubic inches.

Name _____ Date _____

Exercises

1. What is the affect on the area of a circle when the radius is tripled?

   Ⓐ The area is $\frac{1}{3}$ the original area.

   Ⓑ The area is 3 times the original area.

   Ⓒ The area is unchanged.

   Ⓓ The area is 9 times the original area.

2. A square has a side length of 5 meters. What is the affect on the perimeter of the square when the side length is tripled?

   Ⓐ The perimeter is 1.5 times the original perimeter.

   Ⓑ The perimeter is 3 times the original perimeter.

   Ⓒ The perimeter is 6 times the original perimeter.

   Ⓓ The perimeter is 9 times the original perimeter.

3. Jessica cans tomatoes in two sizes of jars. The smaller jar has half the dimensions of the larger jar. If the larger jar has a volume of 430 cubic inches, what is the volume of the smaller jar?

   Ⓐ $53\frac{3}{4}$ in.³

   Ⓑ $107\frac{1}{2}$ in.³

   Ⓒ 215 in.³

   Ⓓ 860 in.³

4. Refer to the rectangle below. What is the area of the rectangle after all side lengths are doubled?

   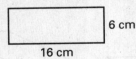
   6 cm
   16 cm

   Ⓐ 96 cm²

   Ⓑ 192 cm²

   Ⓒ 384 cm²

   Ⓓ 576 cm²

5. A square-shaped office has a side length of 90 feet. The owners want to double the dimensions of the space. If the area of the existing space is 8100 square feet, what will be the area of the new office space?

   Ⓐ 48,600 ft²

   Ⓑ 32,400 ft²

   Ⓒ 24,300 ft²

   Ⓓ 16,200 ft²

6. The dimensions of a sphere are increased by a scale factor of 4. The surface area of the original sphere is about 314 cm². What is the surface area of the larger sphere?

   Ⓐ 1256 cm²

   Ⓑ 2512 cm²

   Ⓒ 3768 cm²

   Ⓓ 5024 cm²

7. Mr. Gonzalez needs to increase the space he rents at a boat yard. He currently rents a rectangular storage space of 6000 cubic feet. If he increases the dimensions of the storage space 1.5 times, what will be the volume of the new storage space?

   Ⓐ 9000 ft³

   Ⓑ 13,500 ft³

   Ⓒ 20,250 ft³

   Ⓓ 27,000 ft³

8. Two spheres are similar with a scale factor of 1 : 3. The volume of the smaller sphere is 34 cubic inches. What is the volume of the larger sphere?

   Ⓐ 68 in.³

   Ⓑ 102 in.³

   Ⓒ 306 in.³

   Ⓓ 918 in.³

9. The dimensions of a cone are doubled. If the approximate volume of the cone is 150 cubic meters, what is the volume of the larger cone?

   Ⓐ 300 m³   Ⓑ 600 m³

   Ⓒ 900 m³   Ⓓ 1200 m³

California Standards
Geometry 12.0

Students find and use measures of sides and of interior and exterior angles of triangles and polygons to classify figures and solve problems.

Classifying Triangles and Polygons

Triangle Theorems
Triangle Sum Theorem
The sum of the measures of the interior angles of a triangle is 180°.
Exterior Angle Theorem
The measure of an exterior angle of a triangle is equal to the sum of the measures of the two nonadjacent interior angles.
Base Angles Theorem
If two sides of a triangle are congruent, then the angles opposite them are congruent.
Converse of the Base Angles Theorem
If two angles of a triangle are congruent, then the sides opposite them are congruent.
Converse of the Pythagorean Theorem
If the square of the length of the longest side of a triangle is equal to the sum of the squares of the lengths of the other two sides, then the triangle is a right triangle.
Acute Triangle Theorem
If the square of the length of the longest side of a triangle is less than the sum of the squares of the lengths of the other two sides, then the triangle is an acute triangle.
Obtuse Triangle Theorem
If the square of the length of the longest side of a triangle is greater than the sum of the squares of the lengths of the other two sides, then the triangle is an obtuse triangle.
Equilateral Triangle Theorem (Corollary to the Base Angles Theorem)
If a triangle is equilateral, then it is equiangular. The converse is also true.

Polygon Theorems
Polygon Interior Angles Theorem
The sum of the measures of the interior angles of a convex n-gon is $(n - 2) \cdot 180°$.
Polygon Exterior Angles Theorem
The sum of the measures of the exterior angles of a convex polygon, one angle at each vertex, is 360°.

Example 1

Find Interior Angle Measures in a Triangle

Find the measures of the angles of the triangle shown.

Solution

Use the Triangle Sum Theorem to set up and solve an equation.

$$80 + 3x + 2x + 15 = 180$$
$$5x = 85$$
$$x = 17$$

Substitute the value of x into the angle expressions.

$$m\angle B = 3x = 3(17) = 51°$$
$$m\angle C = 2x + 15 = 2(17) + 15 = 49°$$

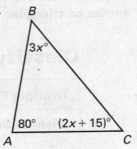

Example 2

Find Exterior Angle Measures in a Triangle

Find $m\angle QRS$.

Solution

Use the Exterior Angle Theorem to set up and solve an equation.

$$3x + 50 = 5x + 2$$
$$48 = 2x$$
$$24 = x$$

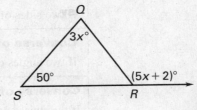

Substitute the value of x into the expression for the exterior angle.

$$5x + 2 = 5(24) + 2 = 122°, \text{ so } m\angle QRS = 180° - 122° = 58°$$

Example 3

Find Side Length

Find the values of x and y in the diagram.

Solution

From the diagram we know that $3y - 1 = 3x^2 + 2$.
Using the Converse of the Base Angles Theorem
we know that $3x^2 + 2 = y + 9$.
So $3x - 1 = y + 9$ by the Transitive Property of Equality.

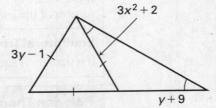

Solve for y.   Use the value of y to find x.

$$3y - 1 = y + 9 \qquad 3x^2 + 2 = y + 9$$
$$2y = 10 \qquad\quad 3x^2 + 2 = 5 + 9$$
$$y = 5 \qquad\qquad 3x^2 = 12$$
$$x^2 = 4$$
$$x = 2 \qquad \textbf{Find the positive square root.}$$

Example 4

Classify Triangles

Can segments with lengths of 9 meters, 10 meters, and 15 meters form a triangle? If so, would the triangle be *acute*, *right*, or *obtuse*?

Solution

STEP 1 Use the Triangle Inequality Theorem to check that the segments can make a triangle.

$9 + 10 = 19$	$9 + 15 = 24$	$10 + 15 = 25$
$19 > 15$	$24 > 10$	$25 > 9$

STEP 2 Classify the triangle by comparing the square of the length of the longest side with the sum of squares of the lengths of the shorter sides.

$c^2 \; \underline{?} \; a^2 + b^2$ **Compare c^2 with $a^2 + b^2$.**

$15^2 \; \underline{?} \; 9^2 + 10^2$ **Substitute.**

$225 \; \underline{?} \; 81 + 100$ **Simplify.**

$225 > 181$ **c^2 is greater than $a^2 + b^2$.**

Answer The side lengths 9 meters, 10 meters, and 15 meters form an obtuse triangle.

Example 5

Find Interior Angle Measures in a Polygon

Find the value of x in the diagram.

Solution

The polygon is a pentagon. Use the Polygon Interior Angles Theorem with $n = 5$ to write an equation involving x. Then solve the equation.

$m\angle 1 + m\angle 2 + m\angle 3 + m\angle 4 + m\angle 5 = (5 - 2) \cdot 180°$

$x° + 107° + 90° + 145° + 76° = 540°$

$x + 418 = 540$

$x = 122$

Answer The value of x is 122.

Example 6

Find Exterior Angle Measures in a Polygon

Find the value of x in the diagram.

Solution

Use the Polygon Exterior Angles Theorem to write an equation involving x. Then solve the equation.

$m\angle 1 + m\angle 2 + m\angle 3 + m\angle 4 = 360°$

$x° + 89° + 108° + 83° = 360°$

$x + 280 = 360$

$x = 80$

Answer The value of x is 80.

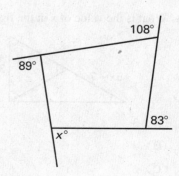

Exercises

1. An exterior angle of a regular polygon measures 90°. What type of figure is the polygon?

(A) triangle

(B) square

(C) pentagon

(D) hexagon

2. In the figure below, an exterior angle of the triangle measures 125°.

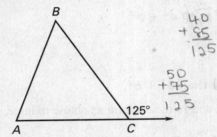

40
+ 85
125

50
+75
125

Which of the following could *not* be the measures of interior angles *A* and *B*?

(A) 50° and 75°

(B) 40° and 85°

(C) 65° and 60°

(D) 45° and 70°

3. The sum of the interior angles of a polygon is twice the sum of its exterior angles. What type of figure is the polygon?

180(n - 2) = 2(360)
180n - 360 = 720
+ 360 + 360
180n = 1080
180   180
n = 6

(A) quadrilateral

(B) hexagon

(C) octagon

(D) nonagon

4. What is the value of *x* in the figure below?

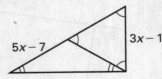

5x - 7   3x - 1

(A) 3

(B) 4

(C) 6

(D) 8

3x - 1 = 5x - 7
+1   +1
3x = 5x - 6
-5x   -5x
-2x = -6
x = 3

5. In the figure below, $\overline{BC} \parallel \overline{AD}$.

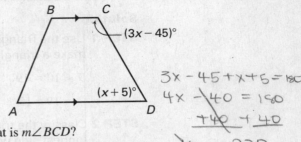

What is $m\angle BCD$?

(A) 55

(B) 60

(C) 120

(D) 165

3x - 45 + x + 5 = 180
4x - 40 = 180
+40   +40
4x = 220
4   4
x = 55

3x - 45 =

6. What type of triangle has side lengths 5 feet, 13 feet, and 16 feet?

$5^2 + 13^2 = 16^2$

(A) acute

(B) isosceles   25 + 169 = ?

(C) right

(D) obtuse

7. The measures of the interior angles of a quadrilateral are $x°$, $3x°$, $5x°$, and $6x°$. What is the measure of the largest interior angle?

$x + 3x + 5x + 6x = 360$

15x = 360
15   15
x = 24

(A) 24°

(B) 72°

(C) 144°

(D) 180°

8. The side lengths of a triangle are 5, *x*, and 13. What are the values of *x* that make the triangle an acute triangle?

(A) $x < 12$

(B) $x > 12$

(C) $x < 8$

(D) $x > 8$

9. In triangle *PQR*, $m\angle P = (4x - 5)°$, $m\angle Q = (8x - 50)°$, and $m\angle R = (3x + 10)°$. Which of the following best describes triangle *PQR*?

(A) right triangle

(B) equilateral triangle

(C) isosceles triangle

(D) scalene triangle

Name _____ Date _____

California Standards
Geometry 13.0

Students prove relationships between angles in polygons by using properties of complementary, supplementary, vertical, and exterior angles.

Angles and Polygons

Terms to Know/Theorems
Two angles are **complementary angles** if the sum of their measures is 90°. Each angle is the *complement* of the other.
Two angles are **supplementary angles** if the sum of their measures is 180°. Each angle is the *supplement* of the other.
Two adjacent angles are a **linear pair** if their noncommon sides are opposite rays. ∠1 and ∠2 are a linear pair. 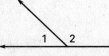
Two angles are **vertical angles** if their sides form two pairs of opposite rays. In the figure, ∠1 and ∠3 are vertical angles. ∠2 and ∠4 are vertical angles. 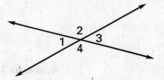

Linear Pair Postulate

If two angles form a linear pair, then they are supplementary.

Vertical Angles Congruence Theorem

Vertical angles are congruent.

Example 1

Find Angle Measures

Find the values of x and y in the diagram.

Solution

By the Exterior Angle Theorem:

$$m\angle AEB = m\angle DAE + m\angle ADE$$
$$x° = 55° + 89°$$
$$x = 144$$

By the Exterior Angle Theorem:

$$m\angle AEB = m\angle BCE + m\angle EBC$$
$$144° = y° + 48°$$
$$y = 96$$

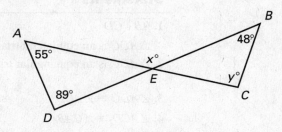

Answer The value of x is 144 and the value of y is 96.

Example 2

Find an Angle Measure

Find the value of x in the diagram.

Solution

By the Base Angles Theorem:

$m\angle TRS = m\angle TSR = 50°$

By the Triangle Sum Theorem:

$m\angle STR + m\angle TSR + m\angle TRS = 180°$

$m\angle STR + 50° + 50° = 180°$

$m\angle STR = 80°$

By the Vertical Angles Congruence Theorem:

$m\angle PTQ = m\angle STR = 80°$

By the Triangle Sum Theorem:

$m\angle PTQ + m\angle PQT + m\angle QPT = 180°$

$80° + 42° + m\angle QPT = 180°$

$m\angle QPT = 58°$

By the Linear Pair Postulate:

$x° + m\angle QPT = 180°$

$x° + 58° = 180°$

$x = 122$

Answer The value of x is 122.

Example 3

Prove Angles are Complementary

GIVEN ▶ $\overline{AB} \parallel \overline{CD}$

$\triangle ADC$ is an equilateral triangle.

PROVE ▶ $\angle ADC$ is complementary to $\angle ABC$.

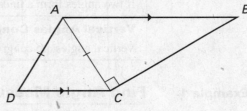

Solution

Statements	Reasons
1. $\overline{AB} \parallel \overline{CD}$ $\triangle ADC$ is an equilateral triangle.	1. Given
2. $\triangle ADC$ is an equiangular triangle.	2. Corollary to the Converse of Base Angles Theorem
3. $\angle ADC \cong \angle ACD$	3. Definition of equiangular triangle
4. $\angle ACD \cong \angle CAB$	4. Alternate Interior Angles Theorem
5. $\angle ADC \cong \angle CAB$	5. Transitive Property of Angle Congruence
6. $m\angle ADC = m\angle CAB$	6. Definition of congruent angles
7. $\angle CAB$ is complementary to $\angle ABC$.	7. The acute angles of a right triangle are complementary.
8. $m\angle CAB + m\angle ABC = 90°$	8. Definition of complementary angles
9. $m\angle ADC + m\angle ABC = 90°$	9. Substitute $m\angle ADC$ for $m\angle CAB$.
10. $\angle ADC$ is complementary to $\angle ABC$.	10. Definition of complementary angles

Exercises

1. What is the measure of an exterior angle of a regular pentagon?

- **A** 36°
- **B** 45°
- **C** 72°
- **D** 90°

2. The figure below shows a tower that was built to support high-voltage power lines. It was designed as an isosceles triangle. If the side of the tower meets the ground at a 98° angle, what is the measure of the angle at the top of the tower?

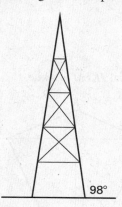

- **A** 8°
- **B** 16°
- **C** 36°
- **D** 41°

3. What is the value of x in the figure below?

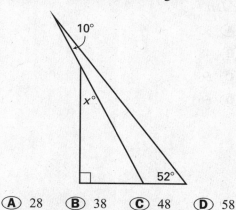

- **A** 28
- **B** 38
- **C** 48
- **D** 58

4. For the figure below, which expression gives the correct value of x in terms of y?

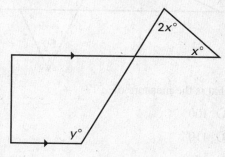

- **A** $x = 3y$
- **B** $x = \dfrac{y}{3}$
- **C** $x = \dfrac{180 - y}{3}$
- **D** $x = \dfrac{y + 90}{3}$

5. What is the value of x in the figure below?

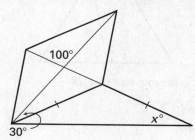

- **A** 25
- **B** 30
- **C** 45
- **D** 50

6. What is the value of x in the figure below?

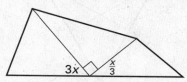

- **A** 9
- **B** 27
- **C** 54
- **D** 81

California Standard Geometry 13.0

7. In the figure below, the measure of ∠2 is 150°.

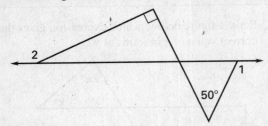

What is the measure of ∠1?

Ⓐ 100°

Ⓑ 110°

Ⓒ 120°

Ⓓ 150°

8. In the figure below, the measures of ∠1, ∠2, and ∠3 are in a 2 : 3 : 4 ratio.

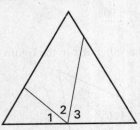

What is the measure of ∠2?

Ⓐ 20°

Ⓑ 40°

Ⓒ 60°

Ⓓ 80°

9. Which additional piece of information would be enough to find the measure of ∠WYZ?

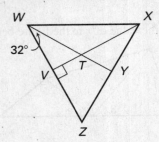

Ⓐ △WXZ is equilateral.

Ⓑ ∠WVT ≅ ∠ZVT

Ⓒ ∠TWX = 30°

Ⓓ $\overline{WZ} \cong \overline{WX}$

10. In the figure below, m∠PQR = 95°.

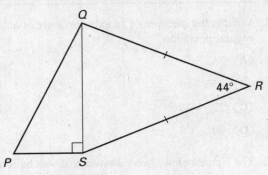

What is m∠QPS?

Ⓐ 32°

Ⓑ 46°

Ⓒ 63°

Ⓓ 68°

11. Quadrilateral JKLM is a kite.

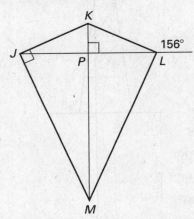

If ∠KJM is a right angle, what is the measure of ∠JML?

Ⓐ 33°

Ⓑ 48°

Ⓒ 56°

Ⓓ 66°

California Standards
Geometry 14.0
Students prove the Pythagorean theorem.

Pythagorean Theorem

Pythagorean Theorem

In a right triangle, the square of the length of the hypotenuse is equal to the sum of the squares of the lengths of the legs.

Example 1

Prove the Pythagorean Theorem

In the figure, the four right triangles are congruent and form a smaller square in the middle. Use this figure to prove the Pythagorean theorem.

Solution

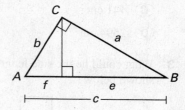

Area of large square = Area of four triangles + Area of smaller square

$(a + b)^2 = 4\left(\frac{1}{2}ab\right) + c^2$ **Use area formulas.**

$a^2 + 2ab + b^2 = 2ab + c^2$ **Multiply.**

$a^2 + b^2 = c^2$ **Subtract 2ab from each side.**

Example 2

Prove the Pythagorean Theorem

GIVEN ▶ In $\triangle ABC$, $\angle BCA$ is a right angle.
PROVE ▶ $c^2 = a^2 + b^2$

Solution

Statements	Reasons
1. $\angle BCA$ is a right angle.	1. Given
2. Draw a perpendicular from C to $\overline{AB}$.	2. Perpendicular Postulate
3. $\frac{c}{a} = \frac{a}{e}$ and $\frac{c}{b} = \frac{b}{f}$	3. Geometric Mean (leg) Theorem
4. $ce = a^2$ and $cf = b^2$	4. Cross Products Property
5. $ce + b^2 = a^2 + b^2$	5. Addition Property of Equality
6. $ce + cf = a^2 + b^2$	6. Substitution Property of Equality
7. $c(e + f) = a^2 + b^2$	7. Distributive Property
8. $e + f = c$	8. Segment Addition Postulate
9. $c \cdot c = a^2 + b^2$	9. Substitution Property of Equality
10. $c^2 = a^2 + b^2$	10. Simplify.

Exercises

1. What is the area of the largest square in the model below?

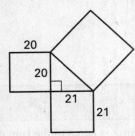

20
20
21
21

Ⓐ 29 units²

Ⓑ 441 units²

Ⓒ 484 units²

Ⓓ 841 units²

2. The model below demonstrates the Pythagorean Theorem. What is the area of b^2?

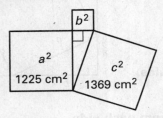

b^2

a^2
1225 cm²

c^2
1369 cm²

Ⓐ 144 cm²

Ⓑ 289 cm²

Ⓒ 441 cm²

Ⓓ 2594 cm²

3. What could be the side lengths of the model shown below?

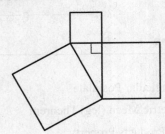

Ⓐ 4, 7.5, 8.5

Ⓑ 8, 12, 15

Ⓒ 12.5, 26, 30

Ⓓ 14, 35, 37

4. The drawing below shows a grass lot shaped like a right triangle surrounded by three square fields. If the perimeter of Field A is 40 meters, and the perimeter of Field B is 96 meters, what is the perimeter of Field C?

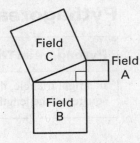

Field
C

Field
A

Field
B

Ⓐ 56 m   Ⓑ 104 m

Ⓒ 136 m   Ⓓ 152 m

5. The drawing shows how three squares can be placed so three of their edges form a triangle. Which set of squares could form a right triangle?

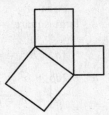

Ⓐ Set 1:

4
4.5
2.5

Ⓑ Set 2:

6
8
6

Ⓒ Set 3:

6.5
2.5
6

Ⓓ Set 4:

5
7
9

Name _____   Date _____

California Standards
Geometry 15.0

Students use the Pythagorean theorem to determine distance and find missing lengths of sides of right triangles.

Using the Pythagorean Theorem

Example 1

Find a Missing Side Length

A 14 foot ladder rests against the side of a house, and the base of the ladder is 5 feet away from the house. Approximately how high above the ground is the top of the ladder?

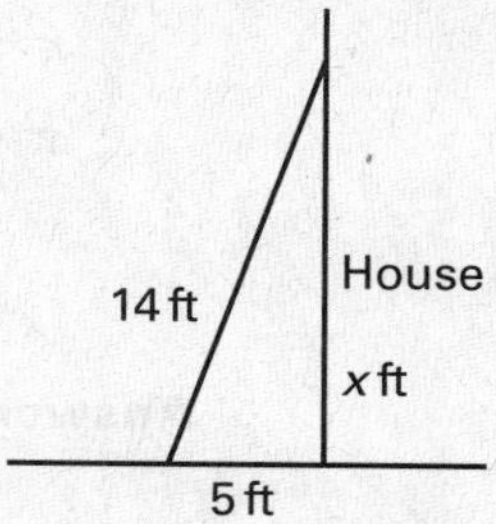

Solution

$$\left(\begin{array}{c}\text{Length} \\ \text{of ladder}\end{array}\right)^2 = \left(\begin{array}{c}\text{Distance} \\ \text{from house}\end{array}\right)^2 + \left(\begin{array}{c}\text{Height} \\ \text{of ladder}\end{array}\right)^2$$

$14^2 = 5^2 + x^2$ **Substitute.**

$196 = 25 + x^2$ **Multiply.**

$171 = x^2$ **Subtract 25 from each side.**

$\sqrt{171} = x$ **Find the positive square root.**

$13.1 \approx x$ **Approximate with a calculator.**

Answer The top of the ladder is approximately 13.1 feet above the ground.

(Diagram: right triangle with hypotenuse labeled 14 ft, vertical side labeled x ft against House, base labeled 5 ft)

Example 2

Find the Perimeter of a Triangle

The diagram represents a rock garden in a park. Kiesha is positioning rocks that are 7.3 inches wide along the edge of the garden to define its border. How many rocks will she need for the entire border?

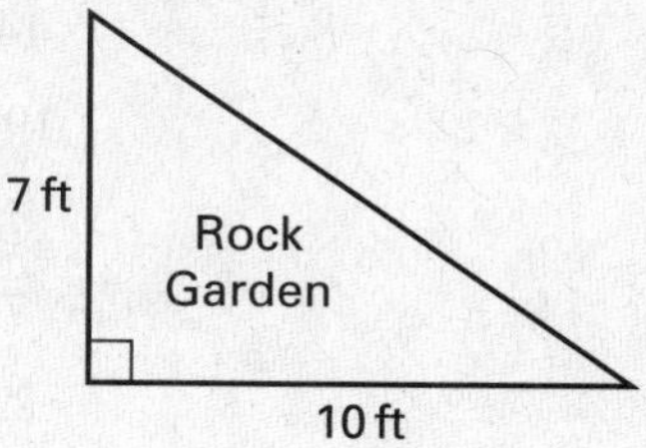

Solution

STEP 1 Find the length of the missing side.

$$\left(\begin{array}{c}\text{Diagonal} \\ \text{of garden}\end{array}\right)^2 = \left(\begin{array}{c}\text{Width} \\ \text{of garden}\end{array}\right)^2 + \left(\begin{array}{c}\text{Length} \\ \text{of garden}\end{array}\right)^2$$

$x^2 = 7^2 + 10^2$ **Substitute.**

$x^2 = 49 + 100$ **Multiply.**

$x^2 = 149$ **Add.**

$x = \sqrt{149} \approx 12.2$ **Find the positive square root.**

STEP 2 Find the perimeter of the garden.

$P = a + b + c = 7 + 10 + 12.2 = 29.2$ ft

STEP 3 Find the number of rocks needed.

$29.2 \text{ ft} \cdot \dfrac{12 \text{ in.}}{1 \text{ ft}} \cdot \dfrac{\text{rock}}{7.3 \text{ in.}} = 48 \text{ rocks}$

Answer Kiesha will need 48 rocks for the border of the garden.

(Diagram: right triangle labeled Rock Garden, vertical side 7 ft, horizontal base 10 ft)

Example 3

Find the Diagonal of a Rectangle

A rose garden in the shape of a rectangle has a diagonal
path from one corner of the garden to the other
corner as shown in the diagram. What is the
approximate length of the diagonal path
through the garden?

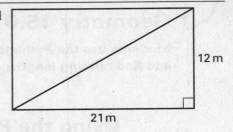

12 m

21 m

Solution

$$\left(\begin{array}{c}\text{Diagonal} \\ \text{of garden}\end{array}\right)^2 = \left(\begin{array}{c}\text{Width} \\ \text{of garden}\end{array}\right)^2 + \left(\begin{array}{c}\text{Length} \\ \text{of garden}\end{array}\right)^2$$

$x^2 = 12^2 + 21^2$ **Substitute.**

$x^2 = 144 + 441$ **Multiply.**

$x^2 = 585$ **Add.**

$x = \sqrt{585} \approx 24.2$ **Find the positive square root.**

Answer The length of the diagonal path through the garden is approximately
24.2 meters.

Example 4

Find the Area of a Rectangle

A laptop computer screen has a diagonal of 14 inches.
The screen is 11 inches wide. What is the approximate area
of the laptop screen?

14 in.

11 in.

Solution

STEP 1 Find the height of the screen.

$$\left(\begin{array}{c}\text{Diagonal} \\ \text{of screen}\end{array}\right)^2 = \left(\begin{array}{c}\text{Width} \\ \text{of screen}\end{array}\right)^2 + \left(\begin{array}{c}\text{Height} \\ \text{of screen}\end{array}\right)^2$$

$14^2 = 11^2 + x^2$ **Substitute.**

$196 = 121 + x^2$ **Multiply.**

$75 = x^2$ **Subtract 121 from each side.**

$\sqrt{75} = x$ **Find the positive square root.**

$8.7 \approx x$ **Approximate with a calculator.**

STEP 2 Find the area of the screen.

$A = w \cdot h \approx 11(8.7) = 95.7$

Answer The area of the laptop screen is approximately 95.7 square inches.

Name _____   Date _____

Exercises

1. The triangle shown below is a right triangle. Which equation must be true?

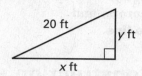

Ⓐ $x^2 + y^2 = 400$ Ⓑ $x^2 + 400 = y^2$

Ⓒ $y^2 + 400 = x^2$ Ⓓ $2x + 2y = 400$

2. The bottom end of a loading ramp is 15 feet from the side of a loading dock. The length of the ramp is 17 feet. What is the height of the dock?

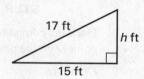

Ⓐ 10 ft   Ⓑ 9 ft   Ⓒ 8 ft   Ⓓ 6 ft

3. A baseball diamond is 90 feet on each side of the infield. To the nearest tenth, how many times farther is it from home plate to second base than from home plate to first base?

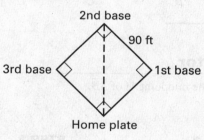

Ⓐ 1.2   Ⓑ 1.3   Ⓒ 1.4   Ⓓ 1.5

4. Wires are used to stabilize a telephone pole that is 50 feet high. A wire from the top of the pole to the ground is 63 feet long. To the nearest tenth of a foot, how far from the bottom of the pole is the wire anchored in the ground?

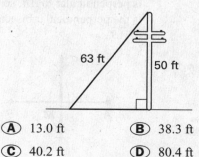

Ⓐ 13.0 ft   Ⓑ 38.3 ft

Ⓒ 40.2 ft   Ⓓ 80.4 ft

5. A surveyor has measured the distances from a point P to the east and west ends of a pond, as shown in the figure below. What is the distance across the pond from east to west?

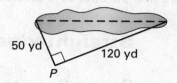

Ⓐ 150 yd   Ⓑ 140 yd

Ⓒ 130 yd   Ⓓ 120 yd

6. A 12 foot ladder rests against the side of a house so the ladder just reaches a window, as shown below. What is the approximate height from the bottom of the window to the ground beneath it?

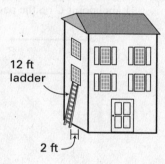

Ⓐ 9 ft   Ⓑ 10 ft

Ⓒ 11.8 ft   Ⓓ 12.2 ft

7. Which of the following dimensions would result in a rectangular quilt that has a diagonal about 12 feet long?

Ⓐ 6.5 ft and 10 ft   Ⓑ 8 ft and 13.5 ft

Ⓒ 7 ft and 11 ft   Ⓓ 9 ft and 3 ft

8. The triangular plot of land shown below will be planted with pine trees. Given that 1 acre = 43,560 square feet, about how many acres will be planted?

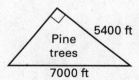

Ⓐ 642   Ⓑ 552   Ⓒ 547   Ⓓ 276

California Standard
Geometry 16.0

California Standards
Geometry 16.0

Students perform basic constructions with a straightedge and compass, such as angle bisectors, perpendicular bisectors, and the line parallel to a given line through a point off the line.

Straightedge and Compass Construction

Example 1   ### Copy a Segment

Construct a segment that is congruent to $\overline{AB}$.

Solution

STEP 1	**STEP 2**	**STEP 3**
Use a straightedge to draw a segment longer than $\overline{AB}$. Label point C on the new segment.	Set your compass to the length of $\overline{AB}$.	Place the compass at C. Mark point D on the new segment. $\overline{CD} \cong \overline{AB}$

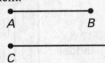

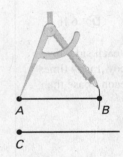

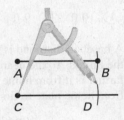

Example 2   ### Construct a Perpendicular Bisector

Construct a perpendicular bisector of $\overline{AB}$ and find the midpoint M of $\overline{AB}$.

Solution

STEP 1	**STEP 2**	**STEP 3**
Place the compass at A. Use a compass setting that is greater than half the length of $\overline{AB}$. Draw an arc.	Keep the same compass setting. Place the compass at B. Draw an arc. It should intersect the other arc at two points.	Use a straightedge to draw a segment through the two points of intersection. This segment bisects $\overline{AB}$ at M, the midpoint of $\overline{AB}$. It can also be proven that this segment is perpendicular to $\overline{AB}$, so it is the perpendicular bisector of $\overline{AB}$.

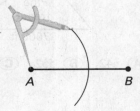

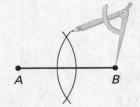

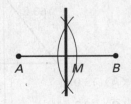

Example 3   ## Copy an Angle

Construct an angle that is congruent to ∠A.

Solution

STEP 1	**STEP 2**	**STEP 3**	**STEP 4**
Draw a segment. Label a point D on the segment.	Draw an arc with center A. Using the same radius, draw an arc with center D.	Label B, C, and E. Draw an arc with radius $\overline{BC}$ and center E. Label the intersection F.	Use a straightedge to draw $\overline{DF}$. ∠EDF ≅ ∠BAC.

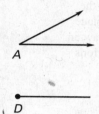 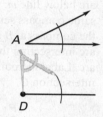 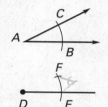 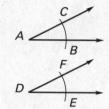

Example 4   ## Construct an Angle Bisector

Construct an angle bisector of ∠A.

Solution

STEP 1	**STEP 2**	**STEP 3**
Place the compass at A. Draw an arc that intersects both sides of the angle. Label the intersections C and B.	Place the compass at C. Draw an arc. Then place the compass point at B. Using the same radius, draw another arc.	Label the intersection G. Use a straightedge to draw a ray through A and G. $\overrightarrow{AG}$ bisects ∠A.

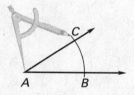 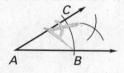 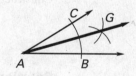

Example 5   ## Construct a Line Parallel to a Given Line

Construct a line through a given point P that is parallel to a given line m.

Solution

STEP 1	**STEP 2**	**STEP 3**
Draw points Q and R on m. Draw $\overrightarrow{PQ}$. Draw an arc with the compass point at Q so it crosses $\overleftrightarrow{QP}$ and $\overrightarrow{QR}$.	Copy ∠PQR on $\overrightarrow{QP}$ with P as the vertex. (See Example 3.)	Label the new angle ∠TPS. Use a straightedge to draw $\overrightarrow{PS}$. $\overleftrightarrow{PS} \parallel \overleftrightarrow{QR}$

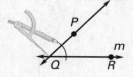 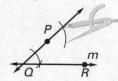 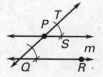

California Standard
Geometry 16.0

Example 6

Construct a Perpendicular to a Line through a Point not on the Line

Construct a line perpendicular to a given line m through a point P that is not on m.

Solution

STEP 1	**STEP 2**	**STEP 3**
Place the compass at P. Draw two arcs intersecting m. Label the intersection points A and B.	Open the compass to a setting greater than $\frac{1}{2}AB$. Place the compass at A, and draw an arc below line m. Using the same compass setting, place the compass at B and draw an arc intersecting the previous arc. Label the point of intersection C.	Use a straightedge to draw $\overleftrightarrow{CP}$. $\overleftrightarrow{CP}$ is perpendicular to $\overleftrightarrow{AB}$.

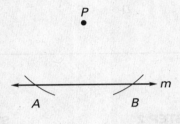

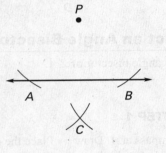

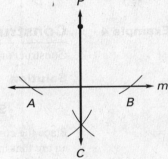

Example 7

Copy an Triangle

Construct a triangle that is congruent to $\triangle ABC$.

Solution

STEP 1	**STEP 2**	**STEP 3**	**STEP 4**
Construct $\overline{DE}$ so that it is congruent to $\overline{AB}$. (See Example 1.)	Open your compass to the length AC. Use this length to draw an arc with the compass point at D.	Draw an arc with radius BC and center E that intersects the arc from Step 2. Label the intersection point F.	Use a straightedge to draw $\triangle DEF$. By the SSS Congruence Postulate, $\triangle ABC \cong \triangle DEF$.

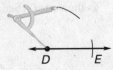

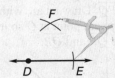

Exercises

1. What is the first step in constructing a line that is perpendicular to a given line *n* and passes through a point *P* not on line *n*?

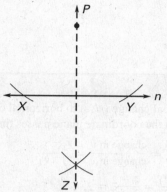

(A) From points *X* and *Y*, draw equal arcs that intersect at *Z*.

(B) Draw $\overleftrightarrow{PZ}$.

(C) From point *P*, draw two arcs that intersect line *n*.

(D) Draw line segments $\overline{PX}$ and $\overline{PY}$.

2. Niki is using a straightedge and compass to complete the construction shown below.

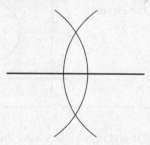

Which of the following *best* describes the construction Nick is completing?

(A) equilateral triangle   WUT

(B) perpendicular bisector of a segment

(C) line parallel to a line through a point

(D) rectangle

3. You are constructing an equilateral triangle with $\overline{AB}$ as one of the sides. Which of the following should be your first step?

(A)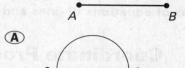

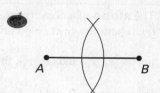

(C)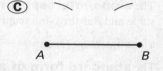

(D)

4. Jason is using a straightedge and compass to complete the construction shown below.

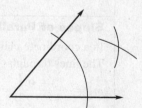

Which *best* describes the construction Jason is completing?

(A) bisecting an angle

(B) bisecting a segment

(C) copying an angle

(D) copying a segment

California Standard
Geometry 16.0

California Standards
Geometry 17.0

Students prove theorems by using coordinate geometry, including the midpoint of a line segment, the distance formula, and various forms of equations of lines and circles.

Coordinate Proofs

Terms to Know

The **slope** of a nonvertical line is the ratio of vertical change (*rise*) to horizontal change (*run*) between any two points on the line. If a line in the coordinate plane passes through

points (x_1, y_1) and (x_2, y_2), then the slope is $m = \dfrac{\text{rise}}{\text{run}} = \dfrac{\text{change in } y}{\text{change in } x} = \dfrac{y_2 - y_1}{x_2 - x_1}$.

For points $(2, 2)$ and $(3, 4)$, $m = \dfrac{\text{change in } y}{\text{change in } x} = \dfrac{y_2 - y_1}{x_2 - x_1} = \dfrac{4 - 2}{3 - 2} = 2$.

The **slope-intercept form of a linear equation** is $y = mx + b$, where m is the slope and b is the y-intercept.

Slope-intercept form: $y = -\dfrac{3}{4}x + 3$

The **standard form of a linear equation** is $Ax + By = C$, where A and B are not both zero.

Standard form: $3x + 4y = 12$

The **standard equation of a circle** with center (h, k) and radius r is $(x - h)^2 + (y - k)^2 = r^2$.

For $(h, k) = (4, 3)$ and $r = 2$, the standard equation of the circle is $(x - 4)^2 + (y - 3)^2 = 4$.

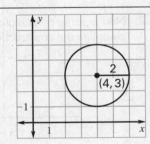

Slopes of Parallel Lines

In a coordinate plane, two nonvertical lines are parallel if and only if they have the same slope. The lines through $(-2, 0)$ and $(-1, 3)$ and through $(0, -3)$ and $(2, 3)$ are parallel.

$m_1 = \dfrac{3 - 0}{-1 - (-2)} = \dfrac{3}{1} = 3$; $m_2 = \dfrac{3 - (-3)}{2 - 0} = \dfrac{6}{2} = 3$; $m_1 = m_2 = 3$

Any two vertical lines are parallel.

Slopes of Perpendicular Lines

In a coordinate plane, two nonvertical lines are perpendicular if and only if the product of their slopes is -1.

The lines through $(1, 3)$ and $(4, 1)$ and through $(4, 1)$ and $(6, 4)$ are perpendicular.

$m_1 = \dfrac{1 - 3}{4 - 1} = -\dfrac{2}{3}$; $m_2 = \dfrac{4 - 1}{6 - 4} = \dfrac{3}{2}$; $m_1 \cdot m_2 = -\dfrac{2}{3} \cdot \dfrac{3}{2} = -1$

Horizontal lines are perpendicular to vertical lines.

Name _____   Date _____

Terms to Know	Example

Midpoint Formula

The coordinates of the midpoint of a segment are the averages of the x-coordinates and of the y-coordinates of the endpoints.

If $A(x_1, y_1)$ and $B(x_2, y_2)$ are points in a coordinate plane, then the midpoint M of $\overline{AB}$ has coordinates

$\left(\dfrac{x_1 + x_2}{2}, \dfrac{y_1 + y_2}{2}\right)$.

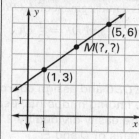

$M\left(\dfrac{x_1 + x_2}{2}, \dfrac{y_1 + y_2}{2}\right)$

$= M\left(\dfrac{1 + 5}{2}, \dfrac{3 + 6}{2}\right)$

$= M\left(\dfrac{6}{2}, \dfrac{9}{2}\right)$

$= M\left(3, \dfrac{9}{2}\right)$

Distance Formula

If $A(x_1, y_1)$ and $B(x_2, y_2)$ are points in a coordinate plane, then the distance between A and B is

$AB = \sqrt{(x_2 - x_1)^2 + (y_2 - y_1)^2}$.

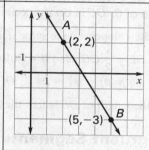

$AB = \sqrt{(x_2 - x_1)^2 + (y_2 - y_1)^2}$

$= \sqrt{(5 - 2)^2 + (-3 - 2)^2}$

$= \sqrt{(3)^2 + (-5)^2}$

$= \sqrt{9 + 25}$

$= \sqrt{34}$

≈ 5.83

Example 1

Write a Coordinate Proof

Prove that $\triangle ABC$ is a right isosceles triangle.

Solution

STEP 1 Prove that two of the sides are congruent.

$AB = 4a$

$AC = \sqrt{(0 - (-2a))^2 + (2a - 0)^2} = \sqrt{4a^2 + 4a^2}$

$\quad = \sqrt{8a^2} = 2a\sqrt{2}$

$BC = \sqrt{(0 - 2a)^2 + (2a - 0)^2} = \sqrt{4a^2 + 4a^2}$

$\quad = \sqrt{8a^2} = 2a\sqrt{2}$

Since $AC = BC$, $\overline{AC} \cong \overline{BC}$.

STEP 2 Prove $\angle ACB$ is a right angle.

Slope of $\overline{AC} = \dfrac{2a - 0}{0 - (-2a)} = \dfrac{2a}{2a} = 1$

Slope of $\overline{BC} = \dfrac{2a - 0}{0 - 2a} = \dfrac{2a}{-2a} = -1$

Since the product of the slopes of $\overline{AC}$ and $\overline{BC}$ is -1, $\overline{AC} \perp \overline{BC}$.

$\triangle ABC$ is a right isosceles triangle.

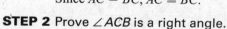

Example 2

Prove the Midsegment Theorem

GIVEN ▶ $\overline{DE}$ is a midsegment of $\triangle OBC$.

PROVE ▶ $\overline{DE} \parallel \overline{OC}$ and $DE = \frac{1}{2} OC$.

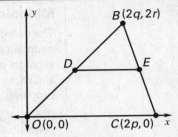

Solution

STEP 1 Place $\triangle OBC$ and assign coordinates. Because you are finding midpoints, use $2p$, $2q$, and $2r$, which are easily divided by 2. Then find the coordinates of D and E.

$$D\left(\frac{2q + 0}{2}, \frac{2r + 0}{2}\right) = D(q, r) \qquad E\left(\frac{2q + 2p}{2}, \frac{2r + 0}{2}\right) = E(q + p, r)$$

STEP 2 Prove $\overline{DE} \parallel \overline{OC}$. The y-coordinates of D and E are the same, so $\overline{DE}$ has a slope of 0. $\overline{OC}$ is on the x-axis, so its slope is 0.

Since their slopes are the same, $\overline{DE} \parallel \overline{OC}$.

STEP 3 Prove $DE = \frac{1}{2} OC$. Use the Ruler Postulate to find DE and OC.

$$DE = |(q + p) - q| = p \qquad OC = |2p - 0| = 2p$$

Since the length of $\overline{DE}$ is half the length of $\overline{OC}$, $DE = \frac{1}{2} OC$.

Example 3

Prove Congruent Segments

GIVEN ▶ $\triangle ABD$ is a right triangle, with the right angle at vertex A. Point C is the midpoint of hypotenuse BD.

PROVE ▶ Point C is the same distance from each vertex of $\triangle ABD$.

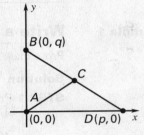

Solution

STEP 1 Place $\triangle ABD$ and assign coordinates. Since C is midpoint of $\overline{BD}$, its coordinates are $\left(\frac{p}{2}, \frac{q}{2}\right)$.

STEP 2 Prove $AC = BC = DC$.

$$AC = \sqrt{\left(\frac{p}{2} - 0\right)^2 + \left(\frac{q}{2} - 0\right)^2} = \sqrt{\frac{p^2}{2^2} + \frac{q^2}{2^2}} = \frac{\sqrt{p^2 + q^2}}{2}$$

$$BC = \sqrt{\left(\frac{p}{2} - 0\right)^2 + \left(\frac{q}{2} - q\right)^2} = \sqrt{\frac{p^2}{2^2} + \frac{q^2}{2^2}} = \frac{\sqrt{p^2 + q^2}}{2}$$

$$DC = \sqrt{\left(\frac{p}{2} - p\right)^2 + \left(\frac{q}{2} - 0\right)^2} = \sqrt{\frac{p^2}{2^2} + \frac{q^2}{2^2}} = \frac{\sqrt{p^2 + q^2}}{2}$$

So, $AC = BC = DC$.

Since $AC = BC = DC$, C is the same distance from each vertex.

California Standard
Geometry 17.0

Exercises

1. The diagram shows quadrilateral *JKLM* with $\overline{JM} \parallel \overline{KL}$.

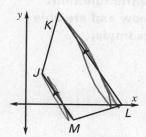

Which statement would prove that quadrilateral *JKLM* is a trapezoid?

- **A** (slope $\overline{JK}$)(slope $\overline{LM}$) = 1
- ⬤ (slope $\overline{JK}$)(slope $\overline{LM}$) = −1
- **C** slope $\overline{JK}$ = slope $\overline{LM}$
- **D** slope $\overline{JK}$ ≠ slope $\overline{LM}$

2. A circle has the equation $(x - 2)^2 + (y + 4)^2 = r^2$. If point $(6, -4)$ lies on the circle, what is the value of *r*?

- ⬤ 4
- **B** 8
- **C** 16
- **D** $4\sqrt{5}$

$(6-2)^2 + (-4+4)^2 = r^2$
$4^2 + 0^2 = r^2$
$r = \sqrt{4^2}$
$r = 4$

3. In △*PQR*, ∠*R* is a right angle. If point *P* has coordinates $(0, 0)$ and point *Q* has coordinates (a, b), which of the following are possible coordinates for point *R*?

- **A** $\left(\frac{a}{2}, \frac{b}{2}\right)$
- **B** (a, a)
- ⬤ $(0, b)$
- **D** (b, b)

4. Figure *DEFG* is a rectangle.

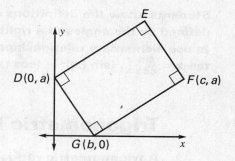

What are the coordinates of *E*?

- ⬤ $\left(\frac{b + c}{2}, 2a\right)$
- **B** $(c - b, 2a)$
- **C** $(b + c, 2a)$
- **D** $\left(\frac{c}{2}, 2a\right)$

5. Which of the following is the equation of a line that passes through the point $(4, -3)$ and is perpendicular to the line $y = \frac{1}{2}x - 3$?

- **A** $y = \frac{1}{2}x - 5$
- **B** $y = -\frac{1}{2}x - 1$
- **C** $y = -2x - 2$
- ⬤ $y = -2x + 5$

$y + 3 = -2(x - 4)$
$y + 3 = -2x + 8$
$-3 \qquad -3$
$y = -2x + 5$

6. Which of the following is the equation of a line that passes through the point $(3, -3)$ and is parallel to the line $y = \frac{1}{3}x + 2$?

- ⬤ $y = \frac{1}{3}x - 4$
- **B** $y = \frac{1}{3}x + 4$
- **C** $y = -3x - 6$
- **D** $y = -3x + 6$

$y + 3 = \frac{1}{3}(x - 3)$
$y + 3 = \frac{1}{3}x - 1$
$-3 \qquad -3$
$y = \frac{1}{3}x - 4$

California Standards
Geometry 18.0

**Students know the definitions of the basic trigonometric functions
defined by the angles of a right triangle. They also know and are able
to use elementary relationships between them. For example,**
$\tan x = \frac{\sin x}{\cos x}$, $(\sin (x))^2 + (\cos (x))^2 = 1$.

Trigonometric Functions

A trigonometric ratio is a ratio of the lengths of two sides in a right triangle.
You will use trigonometric ratios to find the measure of a side or an acute angle in a
right triangle.

Trigonometric Ratios	Example	
Sine Ratio $\sin A = \dfrac{\text{length of leg opposite } \angle A}{\text{length of hypotenuse}}$ $= \dfrac{BC}{AB}$	(triangle JKL, KJ = ⑤, JL = ③, KL = 4)	$\sin K$ $= \dfrac{\text{length of leg opposite } \angle K}{\text{length of hypotenuse}}$ $= \dfrac{JL}{JK} \quad = \dfrac{3}{5}$
Cosine Ratio $\cos A = \dfrac{\text{length of leg adjacent to } \angle A}{\text{length of hypotenuse}}$ $= \dfrac{AC}{AB}$	(triangle JKL, KJ = ⑤, JL = 3, KL = ④)	$\cos K$ $= \dfrac{\text{length of leg adjacent to } \angle K}{\text{length of hypotenuse}}$ $= \dfrac{KL}{JK} \quad = \dfrac{4}{5}$
Tangent Ratio $\tan A = \dfrac{\text{length of leg opposite } \angle A}{\text{length of leg adjacent to } \angle A}$ $= \dfrac{BC}{AC}$	(triangle JKL, KJ = 5, JL = ③, KL = ④)	$\tan K$ $= \dfrac{\text{length of leg opposite } \angle K}{\text{length of leg adjacent to } \angle K}$ $= \dfrac{JL}{KL} \quad = \dfrac{3}{4}$

Trigonometric Identities	Example	
$\tan x = \dfrac{\sin x}{\cos x}$	(triangle JKL, KJ = 5, JL = 3, KL = 4)	$\sin K = \dfrac{3}{5}$, $\cos K = \dfrac{4}{5}$, $\tan K = \dfrac{3}{4}$ $\dfrac{\sin K}{\cos K} = \dfrac{\frac{3}{5}}{\frac{4}{5}} = \dfrac{3}{5} \cdot \dfrac{5}{4} = \dfrac{3}{4} = \tan K$
$(\sin x)^2 + (\cos x)^2 = 1$	(triangle JKL, KJ = 5, JL = 3, KL = 4)	$\sin K = \dfrac{3}{5}$, $\cos K = \dfrac{4}{5}$ $(\sin x)^2 + (\cos x)^2 = \left(\dfrac{3}{5}\right)^2 + \left(\dfrac{4}{5}\right)^2$ $= \dfrac{9}{25} + \dfrac{16}{25} = \dfrac{25}{25} = 1$

Name _____   Date _____

Example 1   ## Find the Sine, Cosine, and Tangent

Find $\sin S$, $\cos S$, and $\tan S$. Then prove the identities
$\tan S = \dfrac{\sin S}{\cos S}$ and $(\sin S)^2 + (\cos S)^2 = 1$ for this triangle.

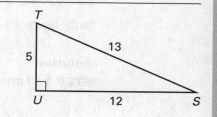

Solution

STEP 1 $\sin S = \dfrac{\text{length of leg opposite } \angle S}{\text{length of hypotenuse}} = \dfrac{TU}{ST} = \dfrac{5}{13}$

$\cos S = \dfrac{\text{length of leg adjacent to } \angle S}{\text{length of hypotenuse}} = \dfrac{US}{ST} = \dfrac{12}{13}$

$\tan S = \dfrac{\text{length of leg opposite } \angle S}{\text{length of leg adjacent to } \angle S} = \dfrac{TU}{US} = \dfrac{5}{12}$

STEP 2 $\dfrac{\sin S}{\cos S} = \dfrac{\frac{5}{13}}{\frac{12}{13}} = \dfrac{5}{13} \cdot \dfrac{13}{12} = \dfrac{5}{12} = \tan S$

STEP 3 $(\sin S)^2 + (\cos S)^2 = \left(\dfrac{5}{13}\right)^2 + \left(\dfrac{12}{13}\right)^2 = \dfrac{25}{169} + \dfrac{144}{169} = \dfrac{169}{169} = 1$

Example 2   ## Find the Sine and Tangent

In the figure, $\cos A = \dfrac{15}{17}$. Find $\sin A$ and $\tan A$.

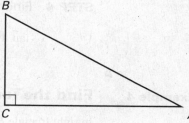

Solution

STEP 1   Label the sides of the triangle.

$\cos A = \dfrac{15}{17} = \dfrac{\text{length of leg adjacent to } \angle A}{\text{length of hypotenuse}}$

length of leg adjacent to $\angle A = 15$

length of hypotenuse $= 17$

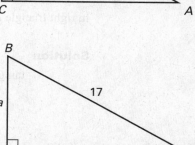

STEP 2   Use the Pythagorean Theorem to find a.

$a^2 + b^2 = c^2$

$a^2 = c^2 - b^2$

$a = \sqrt{c^2 - b^2} = \sqrt{17^2 - 15^2}$

$= \sqrt{289 - 225} = \sqrt{64} = 8$

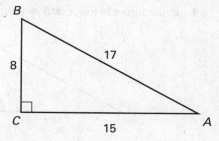

STEP 3   Find $\sin A$.

$\sin A = \dfrac{\text{length of leg opposite } \angle A}{\text{length of hypotenuse}} = \dfrac{a}{17} = \dfrac{8}{17}$

STEP 4   Find $\tan A$.

$\tan A = \dfrac{\text{length of leg opposite } \angle A}{\text{length of leg adjacent to } \angle A} = \dfrac{a}{15} = \dfrac{8}{15}$

Example 3

Find the Cosine and Tangent

In the figure, $\sin A = \frac{2}{3}$. Find $\cos A$ and $\tan A$.

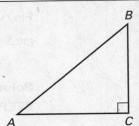

Solution

STEP 1 Label the sides of the triangle.

$$\sin A = \frac{2}{3} = \frac{\text{length of leg opposite } \angle A}{\text{length of hypotenuse}}$$

length of leg opposite $\angle A = 2$

length of hypotenuse $= 3$

STEP 2 Use the Pythagorean Theorem to find b.

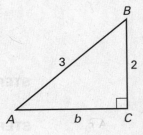

$$a^2 + b^2 = c^2$$
$$b^2 = c^2 - a^2$$
$$b = \sqrt{c^2 - a^2} = \sqrt{3^2 - 2^2} = \sqrt{9 - 4} = \sqrt{5}$$

STEP 3 Find $\cos A$.

$$\cos A = \frac{\text{length of leg adjacent to } \angle A}{\text{length of hypotenuse}} = \frac{b}{3} = \frac{\sqrt{5}}{3}$$

STEP 4 Find $\tan A$.

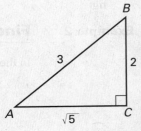

$$\tan A = \frac{\text{length of leg opposite } \angle A}{\text{length of leg adjacent to } \angle A} = \frac{2}{\sqrt{5}} = \frac{2\sqrt{5}}{5}$$

Example 4

Find the Tangent

In right triangle PQR, $\angle P$ is the right angle, $\sin Q = \frac{24}{25}$, and $\cos Q = \frac{7}{25}$. Find $\tan Q$.

Solution

$$\tan Q = \frac{\sin Q}{\cos Q} = \frac{\frac{24}{25}}{\frac{7}{25}} = \frac{24}{25} \cdot \frac{25}{7} = \frac{24}{7}$$

Exercises

1. In the figure below, $\cos B = 0.9$.

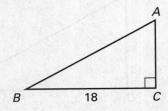

What is the length of $\overline{AB}$?

(A) 8.7   (B) 20

(C) 26.9   (D) 50

2. In right triangle XYZ, $\angle Z$ is the right angle,

$\sin X = \frac{12}{13}$, and $\cos X = \frac{5}{13}$. What is $\tan X$?

(A) $\frac{12}{5}$

(B) $\frac{5}{12}$

(C) $\frac{13}{12}$

(D) $\frac{13}{5}$

3. In the figure below, ∠F is a right angle.

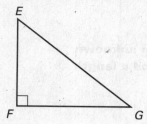

Which expression has the same value as (sin G)²?

Ⓐ (tan G)² + (cos G)²

Ⓑ (tan G)² − (cos G)²

Ⓒ 1 − (cos G)²

Ⓓ 1 + (cos G)²

4. A ramp has the measurements shown in the figure below.

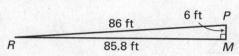

What ratio could be used to find the measure of ∠R, the angle of inclination for the ramp?

Ⓐ $\tan R = \dfrac{6}{86}$

Ⓑ $\sin R = \dfrac{85.8}{86}$

Ⓒ $\cos R = \dfrac{6}{86}$

Ⓓ $\tan R = \dfrac{6}{85.8}$

5. In the figure below, $\cos X = \dfrac{24}{25}$.

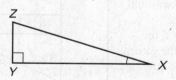

What are sin X and tan X?

Ⓐ $\sin X = \dfrac{24}{25}$ and $\tan X = \dfrac{7}{24}$

Ⓑ $\sin X = \dfrac{25}{7}$ and $\tan X = \dfrac{24}{7}$

Ⓒ $\sin X = \dfrac{7}{25}$ and $\tan X = \dfrac{7}{24}$

Ⓓ $\sin X = \dfrac{7}{25}$ and $\tan X = \dfrac{24}{7}$

6. In the figure below, $\sin Y = \dfrac{2\sqrt{10}}{7}$ and $\cos Y = \dfrac{3}{7}$.

What is tan Y?

Ⓐ $\dfrac{2\sqrt{10}}{3}$

Ⓑ $\dfrac{7\sqrt{10}}{20}$

Ⓒ $\dfrac{7}{3}$

Ⓓ $\dfrac{3\sqrt{10}}{20}$

7. Right triangle PQR is shown below.

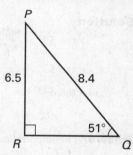

Which equation can be used to find the correct value for QR?

Ⓐ $\sin 51° = \dfrac{6.5}{QR}$

Ⓑ $\cos 51° = \dfrac{QR}{6.5}$

Ⓒ $\sin 39° = \dfrac{QR}{8.4}$

Ⓓ $\tan 39° = \dfrac{8.4}{QR}$

California Standard Geometry 18.0

California Standards
Geometry 19.0

Students use trigonometric functions to solve for an unknown length of a side of a right triangle, given an angle and a length of a side.

Solving Right Triangles

Example 1   ## Estimate Height Using Tangent

Find the height h of the telephone pole to the nearest tenth of a foot.

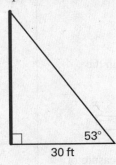

53°
30 ft

Solution

$\tan 53° = \dfrac{\text{opp.}}{\text{adj.}}$ **Write ratio for tangent of 53°.**

$\tan 53° = \dfrac{h}{30}$ **Substitute.**

$30 \cdot \tan 53° = h$ **Multiply each side by 30.**

$39.8 \approx h$ **Use a calculator to simplify.**

Answer The telephone is about 39.8 feet tall.

Example 2   ## Use a Trigonometric Ratio to Find a Hypotenuse

You want to create a triangular garden between a walkway and a driveway, as shown in the diagram. Write and solve a proportion using a trigonometric ratio to approximate x, the length of border material you will need for the edge of the garden.

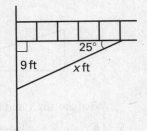

25°
9 ft x ft

Solution

$\sin 25° = \dfrac{\text{opp.}}{\text{hyp.}}$ **Write ratio for sine of 25°.**

$\sin 25° = \dfrac{9}{x}$ **Substitute.**

$x \cdot \sin 25° = 9$ **Multiply each side by x.**

$x = \dfrac{9}{\sin 25°}$ **Divide each side by sin 25°.**

$x \approx \dfrac{9}{0.4226}$ **Use a calculator to find sin 25°.**

$x \approx 21.3$ **Simplify.**

Answer You will need about 21.3 feet of border material.

Example 3

Find a Distance Using an Angle of Elevation

Sam is standing on a city street looking up at the top of a building that is 700 feet tall. The angle of elevation between Sam's line of sight and the horizontal is 74°. His eyes are about 5 ft above the ground. To the nearest foot, how far is Sam from the base of the building?

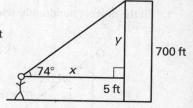

Solution

STEP 1 Find y.

$h = y + 5$	**Write an equation for the height of the building.**
$700 = y + 5$	**Substitute.**
$695 = y$	**Subtract 5 from each side.**

STEP 2 Find the distance x.

$\tan 74° = \dfrac{\text{opp.}}{\text{adj.}}$	**Write ratio for tangent of 74°.**
$\tan 74° = \dfrac{695}{x}$	**Substitute.**
$x \tan 74° = 695$	**Multiply each side by x.**
$x = \dfrac{695}{\tan 74°}$	**Divide each side by tan 74°.**
$x \approx \dfrac{695}{3.4874}$	**Use a calculator to find tan 74°.**
$x \approx 199.3$	**Simplify.**

Answer Sam is standing about 199.3 feet from the base of the building.

Example 4

Find a Height Using an Angle of Depression

A ramp to a loading dock is installed with an angle of depression of 14°. If the ramp is 16.5 feet long, how far is the end of the ramp from the loading dock? Round your answer to the nearest tenth of a foot.

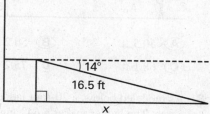

Solution

Find x.

$\cos 14° = \dfrac{\text{adj.}}{\text{hyp.}}$	**Write ratio for cosine of 14°.**
$\cos 14° = \dfrac{x}{16.5}$	**Substitute.**
$16.5 \cos 14° = x$	**Multiply each side by 16.5.**
$16.5 \cdot 0.9703 \approx x$	**Use a calculator to find cos 14°.**
$16.0 \approx x$	**Simplify.**

Answer The end of the ramp is about 16.0 feet from the loading dock.

California Standard Geometry 19.0

Exercises

1. To the nearest hundredth, what is the length of $\overline{PR}$?

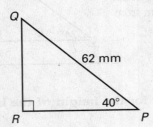

(A) 39.85 mm   (B) 47.49 mm

(C) 52.02 mm   (D) 80.94 mm

2. Corey is flying a kite. He has let 86 feet of string out of his spool and the angle of inclination the kite is making from the horizontal is about 36°. How high is the kite above the ground if he is holding the end of the string at a point 5 feet 8 inches above the ground?

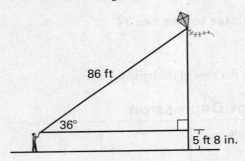

(A) 50.5 ft   (B) 56.2 ft

(C) 68.1 ft   (D) 75.2 ft

3. As modeled below, a 20-foot ladder leans against a tree. The ladder makes a 64° angle with the ground. Which of the following is closest to the distance up the tree the ladder reaches?

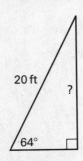

$$\sin 64° \approx 0.90$$
$$\cos 64° \approx 0.44$$
$$\tan 64° \approx 2.05$$

(A) 8.8 ft   (B) 18.0 ft

(C) 22.2 ft   (D) 41.0 ft

4. In the figure below, $m\angle P = 48°$ and $PQ = 15$.

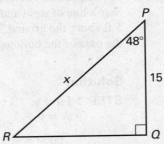

Which equation could be used to find the value of x?

(A) $x = 15 \tan 48°$

(B) $x = \dfrac{15}{\sin 48°}$

(C) $x = \dfrac{15}{\cos 48°}$

(D) $x = \dfrac{15}{\tan 48°}$

5. Triangle *DEF* is shown below.

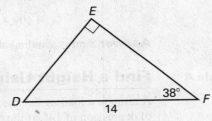

Which equation could be used to find *EF*?

(A) $\sin 38° = \dfrac{14}{EF}$

(B) $\cos 38° = \dfrac{14}{EF}$

(C) $\sin 38° = \dfrac{EF}{14}$

(D) $\cos 38° = \dfrac{EF}{14}$

California Standards
Geometry 20.0

Students know and are able to use angle and side relationships in problems with special right triangles, such as 30°, 60°, and 90° triangles and 45°, 45°, and 90° triangles.

Special Right Triangles

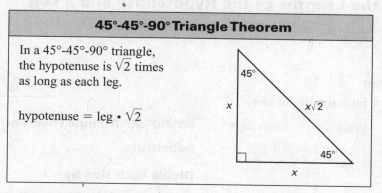

45°-45°-90° Triangle Theorem
In a 45°-45°-90° triangle, the hypotenuse is $\sqrt{2}$ times as long as each leg. hypotenuse = leg • $\sqrt{2}$

Example 1   ## Find the Length of the Hypotenuse

Find the length of the hypotenuse of the triangle in the figure.

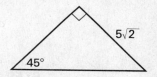

Solution

By the Triangle Sum Theorem, the measure of the third angle must be 45°. The triangle is a 45°-45°-90° triangle. By the 45°-45°-90° Triangle Theorem, the hypotenuse is $\sqrt{2}$ times as long as each leg.

hypotenuse = leg • $\sqrt{2}$	**45°-45°-90° Triangle Theorem**
= $5\sqrt{2} • \sqrt{2}$	**Substitute.**
= 5 • 2	**Product of square roots**
= 10	**Simplify.**

Answer The length of the hypotenuse is 10 units.

Example 2   ## Find the Lengths of the Legs

Find the lengths of the legs of the triangle in the figure.

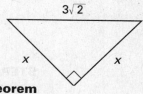

Solution

By the Base Angles Theorem and the Corollary to the Triangle Sum Theorem, the triangle is a 45°-45°-90° triangle.

hypotenuse = leg • $\sqrt{2}$	**45°-45°-90° Triangle Theorem**
$3\sqrt{2} = x • \sqrt{2}$	**Substitute.**
$\frac{3\sqrt{2}}{\sqrt{2}} = \frac{x • \sqrt{2}}{\sqrt{2}}$	**Divide each side by $\sqrt{2}$.**
$3 = x$	**Simplify.**

Answer Each leg has a length of 3 units.

30°-60°-90° Triangle Theorem

In a 30°-60°-90° triangle, the hypotenuse is
twice as long as the shorter leg, and the longer leg
is $\sqrt{3}$ times as long as the shorter leg.

$$\text{hypotenuse} = 2 \cdot \text{shorter leg}$$
$$\text{longer leg} = \text{shorter leg} \cdot \sqrt{3}$$

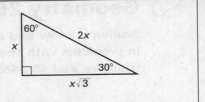

Example 3

Find the Lengths of the Hypotenuse and a Leg

Find the values of x and y. Write your answer in simplest
radical form.

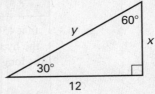

Solution

STEP 1 Find the value of x.

longer leg = shorter leg $\cdot \sqrt{3}$	**30°-60°-90° Triangle Theorem**
$12 = x\sqrt{3}$	**Substitute.**
$\dfrac{12}{\sqrt{3}} = x$	**Divide each side by $\sqrt{3}$.**
$\dfrac{12}{\sqrt{3}} \cdot \dfrac{\sqrt{3}}{\sqrt{3}} = x$	**Multiply numerator and denominator by $\sqrt{3}$.**
$\dfrac{12\sqrt{3}}{3} = x$	**Multiply fractions.**
$4\sqrt{3} = x$	**Simplify.**

STEP 2 Find the value of y.

hypotenuse = 2 $\cdot$ shorter leg	**30°-60°-90° Triangle Theorem**
$y = 2 \cdot 4\sqrt{3} = 8\sqrt{3}$	**Substitute and simplify.**

Example 4

Find the Lengths of the Legs

Find the values of x and y. Write your answer in simplest radical form.

Solution

STEP 1 Find the value of y.

hypotenuse = 2 $\cdot$ shorter leg	**30°-60°-90° Triangle Theorem**
$16\sqrt{3} = 2 \cdot y$	**Substitute.**
$8\sqrt{3} = y$	**Divide and simplify.**

STEP 2 Find the value of x.

longer leg = shorter leg $\cdot \sqrt{3}$	**30°-60°-90° Triangle Theorem**
$x = 8\sqrt{3} \cdot \sqrt{3}$	**Substitute.**
$x = 8 \cdot 3$	**Product of square roots**
$x = 24$	**Simplify.**

California Standard
Geometry 20.0

Name _____ Date _____

Exercises

1. Triangle *DEF* is a right triangle.

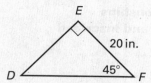

What is the length of $\overline{DF}$?

  Ⓐ 20√3 in.   Ⓑ 40 in.

  Ⓒ 10√2 in.   Ⓓ 20√2 in.

2. Triangle *JKL* is an equilateral triangle.

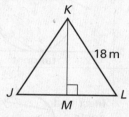

What is the length of $\overline{KM}$?

  Ⓐ 3√3 m   Ⓑ 6√3 m

  Ⓒ 9√3 m   Ⓓ 18√3 m

3. The triangle below is a right triangle.

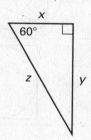

If $y = 5\sqrt{3}$ what is *x*?

  Ⓐ $\frac{5\sqrt{3}}{2}$ Ⓑ 5 Ⓒ 10 Ⓓ 15

4. Triangle *ABC* is shown below. Which equation could be used to find the height *h* of the triangle?

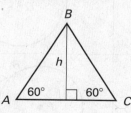

  Ⓐ $h = \frac{\sqrt{3}}{2} BC$ Ⓑ $h = \frac{1}{2} BC$

  Ⓒ $h = \sqrt{2}\, BC$ Ⓓ $h = \sqrt{3}\, BC$

5. The triangle below is a right triangle.

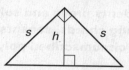

Which equation could be used to find the height *h* of the triangle?

  Ⓐ $h = \frac{1}{2} s$ Ⓑ $h = \frac{\sqrt{3}}{2} s$

  Ⓒ $h = \sqrt{2}\, s$ Ⓓ $h = \frac{\sqrt{2}}{2} s$

6. What is the value of *a* in the triangle below?

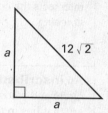

  Ⓐ 6√2 Ⓑ 4√6 Ⓒ 12 Ⓓ 24

7. What is the value of *x*, in feet?

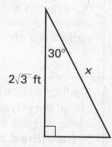

  Ⓐ 2 ft Ⓑ 4 ft Ⓒ 6 ft Ⓓ 8 ft

8. What is the value of *y* in the triangle below?

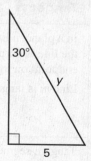

  Ⓐ 10   Ⓑ 10√2

  Ⓒ 5√3   Ⓓ $\frac{5\sqrt{3}}{3}$

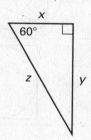

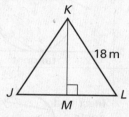

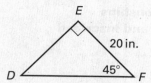

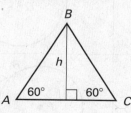

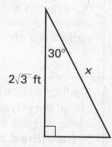

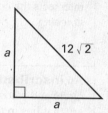

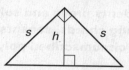

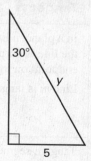

California Standards
Geometry 21.0

Students prove and solve problems regarding relationships among chords, secants, tangents, inscribed angles, and inscribed and circumscribed polygons of circles.

Circles

Terms to Know	Example
A **secant** is a line that intersects a circle in two points. A **tangent** is a line in the plane of a circle that intersects the circle in exactly one point, the *point of tangency*.	secant point of tangency tangent
An **inscribed angle** is an angle whose vertex is on a circle and whose sides contain chords of the circle. The arc that lies in the interior of an inscribed angle and has endpoints on the angle is called the **intercepted arc** of the angle.	inscribed angle intercepted arc
A polygon is an **inscribed polygon** if all of its vertices lie on a circle. The circle that contains the vertices is a **circumscribed circle.**	inscribed triangle
A polygon is a **circumscribed polygon** if every side of the polygon is tangent to a circle. The circle whose tangents make up the circumscribed polygon is an **inscribed circle.**	

Tangents	Example
In a plane, a line is tangent to a circle if and only if the line is perpendicular to a radius of the circle at its endpoint on the circle. Line m is tangent to circle $\odot Q$ if and only if $m \perp \overline{QP}$.	P Q m
Tangent segments from a common external point are congruent. If $\overline{SR}$ and $\overline{ST}$ are tangent segments, then $\overline{SR} \cong \overline{ST}$.	R P S T

Example 1

Use Properties of Tangents

$\overline{PQ}$ is tangent to $\odot T$ at Q and $\overline{PR}$ is tangent to $\odot T$ at R. Find the value of x.

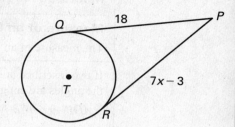

Solution

$\overline{PQ} \cong \overline{PR}$	**Tangent segments from the same point are** $\cong$**.**
$PQ = PR$	**Definition of** $\cong$ **segments**
$18 = 7x - 3$	**Substitute.**
$3 = x$	**Solve for** x**.**

Chords

In the same circle, or in congruent circles, two minor arcs are congruent if and only if their corresponding chords are congruent.

If one chord is a perpendicular bisector of another chord, then the first chord is a diameter.

If $\overline{QS}$ is a perpendicular bisector of $\overline{TR}$, then $\overline{QS}$ is a diameter of the circle.

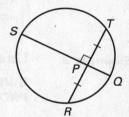

If a diameter of a circle is perpendicular to a chord, then the diameter bisects the chord and its arc.

In the same circle, or in congruent circles, two chords are congruent if and only if they are equidistant from the center.

Example 2

Use Properties of Chords

GIVEN ▶ $\overline{AC} \cong \overline{BC}$, $\angle ACE \cong \angle BCE$
PROVE ▶ $\overline{CD}$ is a diameter of the circle.

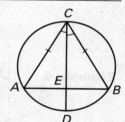

Solution

Statements	Reasons
1. $\overline{AC} \cong \overline{BC}$, $\angle ACE \cong \angle BCE$	1. Given
2. $\overline{CE} \cong \overline{CE}$	2. Reflexive Property of Segment Congruence
3. $\triangle ACE \cong \triangle BCE$	3. SAS Congruence Postulate
4. $\overline{AE} \cong \overline{BE}$; $\angle AEC \cong \angle BEC$	4. Corresponding parts of congruent triangles are congruent.
5. $\overline{CD}$ is the perpendicular bisector of $\overline{AB}$.	5. Definition of perpendicular bisector
6. $\overline{CD}$ is a diameter.	6. If one chord is a perpendicular bisector of another chord, then the first chord is a diameter.

Inscribed Angles and Polygons

Measure of an Inscribed Angle Theorem

The measure of an inscribed angle is one half the measure of its intercepted arc.

If two inscribed angles of a circle intercept the same arc, then the angles are congruent.

$\angle ADB \cong \angle ACB$

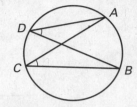

If a right triangle is inscribed in a circle, then the hypotenuse is a diameter of the circle. Conversely, if one side of an inscribed triangle is a diameter of the circle, then the triangle is a right triangle and the angle opposite the diameter is the right angle.

A quadrilateral can be inscribed in a circle if and only if its opposite angles are supplementary.

Example 3

Use Properties of Inscribed Angles

GIVEN ▶ $\odot C$
PROVE ▶ $\triangle YVW \sim \triangle XVZ$

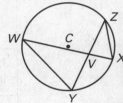

Solution

Statements	Reasons
1. $\odot C$	1. Given
2. $\angle Y \cong \angle X$	2. If two inscribed angles of a circle intercept the same arc, then the angles are congruent.
3. $\angle YVW \cong \angle XVZ$	3. Vertical Angle Congruence Theorem
4. $\triangle YVW \sim \triangle XVZ$	4. AA Similarity Postulate

Example 4

Use Properties of Inscribed Polygons

Find the value of x and y. Then find the measures of the angles in $PQRS$.

Solution

$PQRS$ is inscribed in a circle, so opposite angles are supplementary.

$$m\angle Q + m\angle S = 180° \qquad\qquad m\angle P + m\angle R = 180°$$
$$(2x - 5)° + (3x - 15)° = 180° \qquad 85° + (4y - 5)° = 180°$$
$$5x° - 20° = 180° \qquad\qquad 4y° + 80° = 180°$$
$$5x° = 200° \qquad\qquad 4y° = 100°$$
$$x = 40 \qquad\qquad y = 25$$

$$\angle P = 85°$$
$$\angle Q = (2x - 5)° = (2 \cdot 40 - 5)° = 75°$$
$$\angle R = (4y - 5)° = (4 \cdot 25 - 5)° = 95° \qquad \angle S = (3x - 15)° = (3 \cdot 40 - 15)° = 105°$$

Angles and Segments

If a tangent and a chord intersect at a point on a circle, then the measure of each angle formed is one half the measure of its intercepted arc.

Angles Inside the Circle Theorem

If two chords intersect *inside* a circle, then the measure of each angle is one half the *sum* of the measures of the arcs intercepted by the angle and its vertical angle.

$$m\angle 1 = \frac{1}{2}\left(m\,\widehat{DC} + m\,\widehat{AB}\right)$$

$$m\angle 2 = \frac{1}{2}\left(m\,\widehat{AD} + m\,\widehat{BC}\right)$$

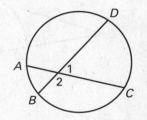

Angles Outside the Circle Theorem

If a tangent and a secant, two tangents, or two secants intersect *outside* a circle, then the measure of the angle formed is one half the *difference* of the measures of the intercepted arcs.

Segments of Chords Theorem

If two chords intersect in the interior of a circle, then the product of the lengths of the segments of one chord is equal to the product of the lengths of the segments of the other chord.

$EA \cdot EB = EC \cdot ED$

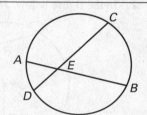

Segments of Secants Theorem

If two secant segments share the same endpoint outside a circle, then the product of the lengths of one secant segment and its external segment equals the product of the lengths of the other secant segment and its external segment.

Segments of Secants and Tangents Theorem

If a secant segment and a tangent share an endpoint outside a circle, then the product of the lengths of the secant segment and its external segment equals the square of the length of the tangent segment.

Example 5

Use Angle and Segment Relationships

Find the value of *a* and *z*.

Solution

$a° = \frac{1}{2}\left(m\,\widehat{AC} + m\,\widehat{BD}\right)$ **Use Angles Inside the Circle Theorem.**

$a° = \frac{1}{2}(148° + 132°)$ **Substitute.**

$a = 140$ **Simplify.**

$AE \cdot EB = DE \cdot EC$ **Use Segments of Chords Theorem.**

$4 \cdot z = 3 \cdot 16$ **Substitute.**

$4z = 48$ **Simplify.**

$z = 12$ **Solve for *z*.**

Exercises

1. In the figure below, secant $\overline{AC}$ intersects the circle at B and secant $\overline{EC}$ intersects the circle at D.

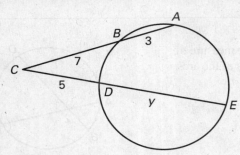

What is the value of y?

(A) 4.2   (B) 5   (C) 9   (D) 9.8

2. In the figure below, JK = LM = 32.

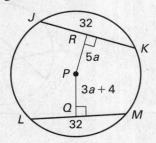

What is PQ?

(A) 2   (B) 4   (C) 10   (D) 20

3. In the circle below, $\overline{DF}$ is a diameter and $m\widehat{EF} = 124°$.

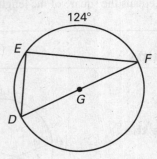

What is $m\angle DFE$?

(A) 28°   (B) 34°   (C) 56°   (D) 62°

4. In the figure, $\overline{PR}$ and $\overline{QS}$ are chords intersecting at T.

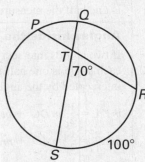

If $m\angle STR = 70°$ and $m\widehat{SR} = 100°$, what is $m\widehat{PQ}$?

(A) 15°   (B) 30°   (C) 35°   (D) 40°

5. In the figure below, secant $\overline{XZ}$ intersects the circle at Y and $\overline{XW}$ is tangent to the circle at W.

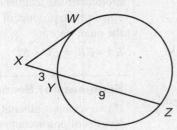

If XY = 3 and YZ = 9, what is XW?

(A) $2\sqrt{3}$ (B) $3\sqrt{3}$ (C) 6   (D) 12

6. $\triangle JKL$ is inscribed in the circle below.

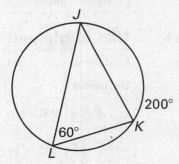

If $m\angle JLK = 60°$ and $m\widehat{JKL} = 200°$, what is $m\angle LJK$?

(A) 40°   (B) 30°   (C) 20°   (D) 10°

California Standards
Geometry 22.0

Students know the effect of rigid motions on figures in the
coordinate plane and space, including rotations, translations,
and reflections.

Transformations

Terms to Know	Example
A **transformation** is an operation that moves or changes a geometric figure in some way to produce a new figure. The new figure is called the **image.** Another name for the original image is the **preimage.**	$\triangle ABC \rightarrow \triangle A'B'C'$ The order of the vertices in the transformation tells you that A' is the image of A, B' is the image of B, and C' is the image of C.
A **translation** moves every point of a figure the same distance in the same direction.	$(x, y) \rightarrow (x + a, y + b)$
A **reflection** uses a line like a mirror to reflect an image. The mirror line is called the **line of reflection.**	Reflection in the x-axis $\quad$ Reflection in the y-axis $(x, y) \rightarrow (x, -y)$ $\qquad$ $(x, y) \rightarrow (-x, y)$
A **rotation** turns a figure about a fixed point, called the **center of rotation.** The **angle of rotation** is formed by rays drawn from the center of rotation through corresponding points on the original figure and its image.	90° clockwise rotation $\quad$ 60° counterclockwise rotation

California Standard
Geometry 22.0

Example 1   ## Translate a Figure in the Coordinate Plane

Figure *PQRS* has vertices $P(-4, 1)$, $Q(-3, 2)$, $R(-1, 2)$, and $S(-3, -2)$. Sketch *PQRS* and its image after the translation $(x, y) \rightarrow (x + 5, y - 3)$.

Solution

First graph *PQRS*. Find the translation of each vertex by adding 5 to its x coordinate and subtracting 3 from its y-coordinate. Then draw the image of *PQRS*.

$(x, y) \rightarrow (x + 5, y - 3)$ $P(-4, 1) \rightarrow P'(1, -2)$

$Q(-3, 2) \rightarrow Q'(2, -1)$

$R(-1, 2) \rightarrow R'(4, -1)$

$S(-3, -2) \rightarrow S'(2, -5)$

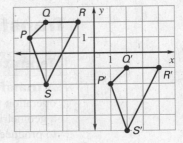

Example 2   ## Reflect a Figure in the Coordinate Plane

The vertices of $\triangle DEF$ are $D(2, 3)$, $E(4, 5)$, and $F(6, 4)$. Graph the reflection of $\triangle DEF$ in the line m: $y = 2$.

Solution

First graph $\triangle DEF$.

Point D is 1 unit above m, so D' is 1 unit below m at $(2, 1)$.

Point E is 3 units above m, so E' is 3 units below m at $(4, -1)$.

Point F is 2 units above m, so F' is 2 units below m at $(6, 0)$.

Use the vertices to draw the image.

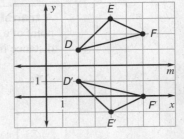

Coordinate Rules for Reflections

If (a, b) is reflected in the x-axis, its image is the point $(a, -b)$.

If (a, b) is reflected in the y-axis, its image is the point $(-a, b)$.

If (a, b) is reflected in the line $y = x$, its image is the point (b, a).

If (a, b) is reflected in the $y = -x$, its image is the point $(-b, -a)$.

Example 3   ## Reflect a Figure Using the Coordinate Rules

You are drawing a pattern for a quilt. Use a reflection in the y-axis to draw the other half of the pattern.

Solution

Multiply the x-coordinate of each vertex by -1 to find the corresponding vertex in the image.

$(a, b) \rightarrow (-a, b)$

$(0, 3) \rightarrow (0, 3)$; $(1, 1) \rightarrow (-1, 1)$; $(4, 0) \rightarrow (-4, 0)$;

$(4, -2) \rightarrow (-4, -2)$; $(0, -3) \rightarrow (0, -3)$

Use the vertices to draw the image.

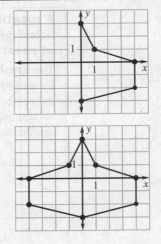

Coordinate Rules for Rotation about the Origin

When a point (a, b) is rotated counterclockwise about the origin, the following are true:

For a rotation of 90°, $(a, b) \rightarrow (-b, a)$.

For a rotation of 180°, $(a, b) \rightarrow (-a, -b)$.

For a rotation of 270°, $(a, b) \rightarrow (b, -a)$.

Example 4

Rotate a Figure Using the Coordinate Rules

Graph quadrilateral $ABCD$ with vertices $A(1, 4)$, $B(2, 5)$, $C(4, 4)$, and $D(2, 1)$. Then rotate the quadrilateral 90° about the origin.

Solution

Graph $ABCD$. Use the coordinate rule for a 90° rotation to find the images of the vertices.

$(a, b) \rightarrow (-b, a)$

$A(1, 4) \rightarrow A'(-4, 1)$; $B(2, 5) \rightarrow B'(-5, 2)$

$C(4, 4) \rightarrow C'(-4, 4)$; $D(2, 1) \rightarrow D'(-1, 2)$

Use the vertices to draw the image.

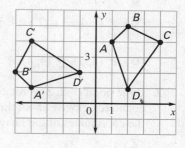

Exercises

1. Under a transformation, the image of point $G(3, 0)$ is $G'(-3, 0)$. Which statement describes this transformation?

  A Rotation of 90° counterclockwise

  B Rotation of 90° clockwise

  C Reflection over the x-axis

  D Reflection over the y-axis

2. What is the line of reflection for the transformation shown below?

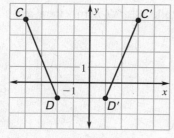

  A $y = -0.5$ **B** $x = 0.5$

  C $x = -0.5$ **D** $x = 0$

3. Brayton is going to rotate point $X(8, -3)$ 90° counterclockwise about point $Y(3, 2)$. What are the coordinates of X'?

  A $X'(8, 7)$

  B $X'(-2, -3)$

  C $X'(-3, 8)$

  D $X'(-8, -7)$

4. The shortest distance between point W and a line of reflection is 64 inches. What will be the distance between W and its image W''?

  A 8 in.   **B** 32 in.

  C 64 in.   **D** 128 in.

5. In pentagon $GHJKL$, the coordinates of H are $(-4, 5)$. What are the coordinates of the image of H after a rotation 180° counterclockwise about the origin?

  A $H'(-4, -5)$

  B $H'(4, -5)$

  C $H'(-5, -4)$

  D $H'(5, 4)$

Exercises

6. Rectangle *PQRS* is shown below.

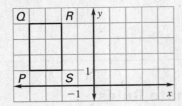

If this rectangle is reflected across the *y*-axis, what will be the coordinates of the vertices for the image *P'Q'R'S'*?

Ⓐ $P'(1,-4), Q'(-4, 4), R'(4, -2), S'(1, -2)$

Ⓑ $P'(1, 4), Q'(4, 4), R'(4, 2), S'(1, 2)$

Ⓒ $P'(-4,-1), Q'(-4, -4), R'(-2, -4),$
    $S'(-2, -1)$

Ⓓ $P'(4, 1), Q'(4, 4), R'(2, 4), S'(2, 1)$

7. If the point $(-2, 3)$ is rotated $180°$ counterclockwise about the origin, what will be the coordinates of the image?

Ⓐ $(-2, -3)$

Ⓑ $(3, 2)$

Ⓒ $(2, -3)$

Ⓓ $(-3, -2)$

8. What are the coordinates of $\triangle F'G'H'$ if $\triangle FGH$ is translated 3 units up and 1 unit to the left?

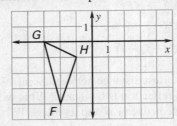

Ⓐ $F'(-2, -4), G'(-3, 0), H'(-1, -1)$

Ⓑ $F'(-1, -3), G'(-4, 3), H'(2, -2)$

Ⓒ $F'(-3, -1), G'(-4, 3), H'(-2, 2)$

Ⓓ $F'(1, -5), G'(0 ,-1), H'(2, -2)$

9. Polygon *HJKL* is the image of *PQRS* after a translation.

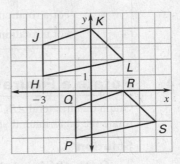

What is the translation?

Ⓐ Move 4 units right and 2 units down.

Ⓑ Move 2 units left and 4 units up.

Ⓒ Move 3 units right and 4 units down.

Ⓓ Move 2 units left and 2 units down.

10. Emily wants to transform $\triangle JKL$ so that $\triangle J'K'L'$ has the coordinates $J'(-3, 5)$, $K'(0, 4)$, and $L'(-5, 1)$.

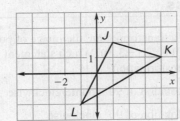

Which transformation should she perform?

Ⓐ Translate $\triangle JKL$ 4 units left and 3 units up.

Ⓑ Rotate $\triangle JKL$ counterclockwise $90°$.

Ⓒ Reflect $\triangle JKL$ across the *x*-axis.

Ⓓ Reflect $\triangle JKL$ across the *y*-axis.

California Standards Review and Practice

Intensive Review

California Standards
Pretest

DIRECTIONS

Read each question. Then, on your answer sheet, fill in the bubble for the correct answer.

1. A diagram from a proof of the Pythagorean theorem is pictured below. Which statement would *not* be used in the proof of the Pythagorean theorem?

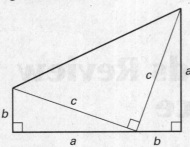

(A) The circumference of the trapezoid is $2a + 2b + c$.

(B) The area of a triangle is $\frac{1}{2} ab$.

(C) The area of the trapezoid is $\frac{(a + b)(a + b)}{2}$.

(D) The sum of the areas of the triangles is equal to the area of the trapezoid.

2. If $a = 6$ feet and $c = 10$ feet in the right triangle below, what is the value of the missing length?

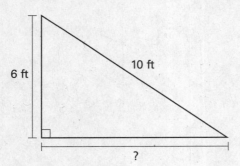

(A) 17 ft   (B) 8 ft   (C) 15 ft   (D) 21 ft

3. A rope stretches from the top of a 20-foot pole to a point 10 feet from the bottom of the pole. How long is the rope?

(A) 30 ft   (B) $10\sqrt{5}$ ft

(C) $10 + \sqrt{500}$ ft   (D) $30 + \sqrt{500}$ ft

4. Mr. Guzman fully extended his 18-foot ladder, so that the top of the ladder just reached the top of his house. The distance from the house to the base of the ladder was 12 feet. To the nearest tenth of a foot, what is the height of Mr. Guzman's house?

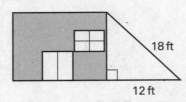

(A) 12.0 ft   (B) 13.4 ft

(C) 18.0 ft   (D) 21.6 ft

5. Which lines are parallel?

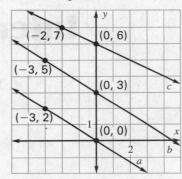

(A) $a \parallel c$ (B) $b \parallel c$

(C) $a \parallel b$ (D) $a \parallel b \parallel c$

6. What is the diameter of $\odot C$?

(A) 3   (B) 4

(C) 6   (D) 8

California Standards
Pretest *continued*

7. If $XY = 9$, $YZ = 7$, and $XZ = 10$, what is the radius of $\odot X$?

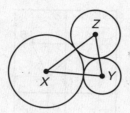

(A) 2 units   (B) 5 units

(C) 6 units   (D) 9 units

8. *PRLG* is a parallelogram with side $PR = 14$ and an area of 112. What statement can be used to find the height, h?

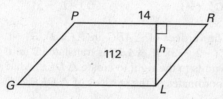

(A) area of a parallelogram = $PR \times h$

(B) area of a parallelogram = PR^2

(C) area of a parallelogram = $PR - RL$

(D) area of a parallelogram = $PR^2 - RL^2$

9. In the figure, the railroad track represents a transversal to the lines that represent the sides of Pine Street. The sides of the street are parallel. Which statement can be justified by the Corresponding Angles Postulate?

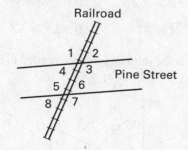

(A) $\angle 4 \cong \angle 8$ (B) $\angle 5 \cong \angle 7$

(C) $\angle 4 \cong \angle 6$ (D) $\angle 1 \cong \angle 7$

10. Two sides of a triangle have sides 5 and 20. The length of the third side must be greater than _____ and less than _____.

(A) 5, 20   (B) 15, 25   (C) 14, 26   (D) 4, 21

11. When the sun is 30° above the horizon, a stick casts a shadow that is 3 meters long. Which equation could be used to find x in $\triangle ABC$, where $x = BC$?

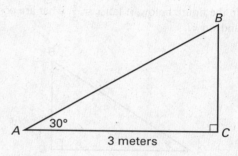

(A) $x = 3 \tan 30°$ (B) $x = 3 \sin 30°$

(C) $x = 3 \cos 30°$ (D) $x = 3 \cotan 30°$

12. If $\tan \angle CBA = \dfrac{AC}{CB}$, find AB.

(A) 28   (B) 17   (C) 15   (D) 8

13. If $\tan \angle BAC = \dfrac{CB}{AB}$, find AB.

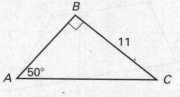

(A) 5.5   (B) 9.2   (C) 14.4   (D) 15.7

14. What is the sine of $\angle R$?

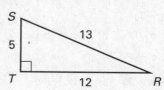

(A) $\dfrac{5}{12}$ (B) $\dfrac{5}{13}$ (C) $\dfrac{12}{13}$ (D) $\dfrac{13}{5}$

California Standards
Pretest *continued*

15. What is the tangent of ∠Z in the triangle shown?

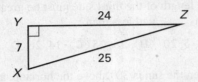

Ⓐ $\frac{7}{25}$ Ⓑ $\frac{7}{24}$ Ⓒ $\frac{24}{25}$ Ⓓ $\frac{25}{24}$

16. In the figure below, if $\tan x = \frac{4}{3}$, what are $\cos x$ and $\sin x$?

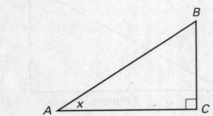

Ⓐ $\cos x = \frac{4}{5}$, $\sin x = \frac{3}{5}$

Ⓑ $\cos x = \frac{3}{5}$, $\sin x = \frac{4}{5}$

Ⓒ $\cos x = \frac{3}{4}$, $\sin x = \frac{5}{4}$

Ⓓ $\cos x = \frac{5}{3}$, $\sin x = \frac{5}{4}$

17. If quadrilateral *EFGH* were reflected about the *x*–axis to form *E'F'G'H'*, what would be the coordinates of *E'*?

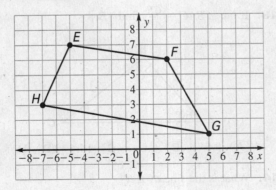

Ⓐ (5, −7)

Ⓑ (5, 7)

Ⓒ (−5, 7)

Ⓓ (−5, −7)

18. △ABC is rotated 180° about the line $y = -1$. What are the coordinates of A'?

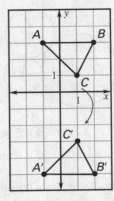

Ⓐ (2, −5)   Ⓑ (1, −1)

Ⓒ (−1, −5)   Ⓓ (1, −5)

19. The vertices of △ABC are A (3, 2), B(−1, 6), and C(−2, −3). If △ABC is translated 2 units up and 5 units to the right to create △DEF, what are the coordinates of the vertices of △DEF?

Ⓐ D(−2, 0), E(−6, 4), F(−7, −5)

Ⓑ D(−2, 0), E(−3, 1), F(−7, −5)

Ⓒ D(4, 8), E(8, 4), F(−1, 3)

Ⓓ D(8, 4), E(4, 8), F(3, −1)

20. In △LMN and △XYZ, $\overline{NL}$ and $\overline{ZX}$ are congruent, and ∠M and ∠Y are congruent. Which additional information would be enough to prove that △LMN ≅ △XYZ?

Ⓐ ∠L ≅ ∠Z   Ⓑ ∠N ≅ ∠Z

Ⓒ $\overline{LM} ≅ \overline{XY}$ Ⓓ $\overline{LN} ≅ \overline{XZ}$

21. What is the third congruence needed to prove that ∠MNQ ≅ ∠PNO by ASA?

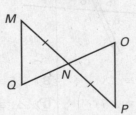

Ⓐ ∠Q ≅ ∠P   Ⓑ ∠MNQ ≅ ∠PNO

Ⓒ ∠M ≅ ∠O   Ⓓ ∠M ≅ ∠P

California Standards
Pretest

California Standards
Pretest *continued*

22. *KITE* is a kite. What is $m\angle K$?

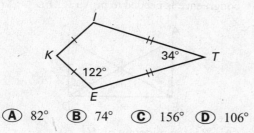

Ⓐ 82° Ⓑ 74° Ⓒ 156° Ⓓ 106°

23. What is $m\angle K$?

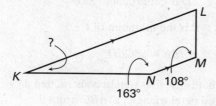

Ⓐ 123° Ⓑ 17° Ⓒ 25° Ⓓ 31°

24. Magglio inscribes a triangle in the given circle with center *C*, as shown. What is the radius of the circle?

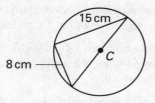

Ⓐ 7 cm   Ⓑ 8.5 cm

Ⓒ 18.5 cm   Ⓓ 23 cm

25. What is the measure of $\angle ACB$?

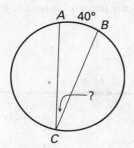

Ⓐ 10° Ⓑ 30° Ⓒ 20° Ⓓ 60°

26. What is the measure of $\angle ADC$?

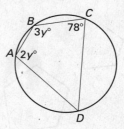

Ⓐ 23° Ⓑ 27° Ⓒ 32° Ⓓ 36°

27. Two chords intersect inside a circle. $AE = 9$, $BE = 12$, and $CD = 24$. What is the length of *CE*?

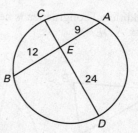

Ⓐ 6   Ⓑ 8   Ⓒ 10   Ⓓ 16

28. In the figure below, what is the measure of $\angle GHI$?

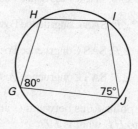

Ⓐ 90° Ⓑ 75° Ⓒ 80° Ⓓ 105°

29. In the diagram, *G* is the incenter of $\triangle ABC$. Which pair of segments is congruent?

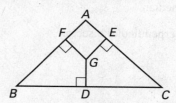

Ⓐ $\overline{BG}$ and $\overline{CG}$ Ⓑ $\overline{AF}$ and $\overline{AE}$

Ⓒ $\overline{AG}$ and GD Ⓓ $\overline{FG}$ and $\overline{DG}$

California Standards Pretest

California Standards
Pretest continued

30. These polygons are similar. Which relationship is true?

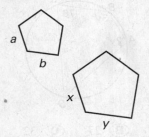

(A) $\dfrac{a}{x} = \dfrac{b}{y}$ (B) $\dfrac{a}{y} = \dfrac{x}{b}$

(C) $ax = by$ (D) $ab = xy$

31. Which additional congruence is needed to prove △ABC ≅ △DEF?

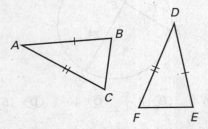

(A) ∠A ≅ ∠D; SAS Congruence Postulate

(B) ∠B ≅ ∠E; SAS Congruence Postulate

(C) ∠C ≅ ∠F; SAS Congruence Postulate

(D) ∠B ≅ ∠F; SAS Congruence Postulate

32. In △FGH, point J lies between G and H. If $\overline{GJ}$ is congruent to $\overline{HJ}$, what is $\overline{FJ}$?

(A) an altitude

(B) an angle bisector

(C) a median

(D) a perpendicular bisector

33. In the diagram below, which additional congruence is needed to prove △AED ≅ △CDE?

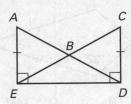

(A) B is the midpoint of $\overline{AD}$.

(B) $\overline{ED}$ is congruent to $\overline{ED}$.

(C) B is the midpoint of $\overline{CE}$.

(D) ∠ABE ≅ ∠CBD

34. What is the first step in constructing an equilateral triangle, △ABC, from the segment AB?

A ——————— B

(A) Draw segment AC where point C is below line AB and length of $\overline{AC}$ = length of $\overline{AB}$.

(B) Draw segment BC where point C is above line AB and length of $\overline{BC}$ = length of $\overline{AB}$.

(C) Set the compass radius to AB. From point A, draw a 90° arc through point B above segment AB.

(D) Find the midpoint of segment AB by drawing an arc from points A and B.

35. You have used your compass and straightedge to construct a line that is perpendicular to $\overline{AB}$ and passes through point C. Through which other point does the perpendicular line pass?

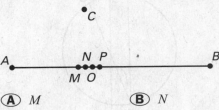

(A) M   (B) N

(C) O   (D) P

California Standards
Pretest *continued*

36. If you construct a line that bisects $\overline{AB}$ using a compass and a straightedge, which other point lies on this line?

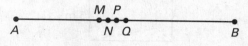

  Ⓐ M Ⓑ N Ⓒ P Ⓓ Q

37. George is constructing a line parallel to line PQ that passes through point R. Which of the following should be his first step?

Ⓐ
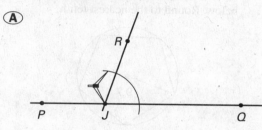

Ⓑ

Ⓒ
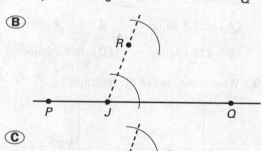

Ⓓ
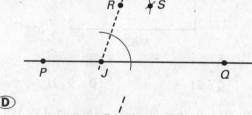

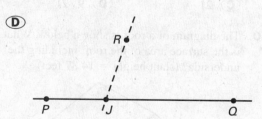

38. Find the coordinates of the other endpoint of a segment with endpoint $X(-2, 3)$ and midpoint $M(1, -2)$.

  Ⓐ $(4, -7)$ Ⓑ $(-4, 7)$

  Ⓒ $(0, -1)$ Ⓓ $(-5, 8)$

39. The diagram shows $\triangle ABC$. If the slope of $\overline{AB} = 2$, and the slope of $\overline{BC} = -\frac{1}{2}$, what type of triangle is $\triangle ABC$?

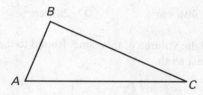

  Ⓐ right triangle

  Ⓑ isosceles triangle

  Ⓒ equilateral triangle

  Ⓓ obtuse triangle

40. The diagram shows circle O inscribed in $\triangle ABC$. If $\triangle ABC$ is an equilateral triangle find the radius in terms of the side length.

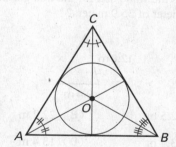

  Ⓐ radius $= 3 \times \dfrac{\text{Side}}{2\sqrt{3}}$

  Ⓑ radius $= \dfrac{\text{Side}}{2\sqrt{3}}$

  Ⓒ radius $= \dfrac{\text{Side}}{2}$

  Ⓓ radius $= 3 \times \dfrac{\text{Side}}{2}$

41. Ray made 2 solid, cylindrical tables for his little sister's dollhouse. The first table is 5 centimeters high and has a diameter of 2 centimeters. The second table is also 5 centimeters high but has a diameter of 4 centimeters. How much more wood did Ray need to make the second table? (Use $\pi = 3.14$.)

  Ⓐ 10 cm^3 Ⓑ 25 cm^3

  Ⓒ 47 cm^3 Ⓓ 8 cm^3

California Standards
Pretest *continued*

42. Find the surface area of a tennis ball, given that the radius is 3.5 centimeters. Round to the nearest unit.

- (A) 16π cm^2
- (B) 51.2π cm^2
- (C) 49π cm^2
- (D) 28π cm^2

43. Find the volume of this cone. Round to the nearest tenth.

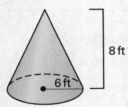

- (A) 96.0 ft^3
- (B) 301.4 ft^3
- (C) 904.3 ft^3
- (D) 50.2 ft^3

44. What is the value of x for the triangle shown with a perimeter of 35.9 meters?

- (A) 32.5 m
- (B) 22.2 m
- (C) 13.7 m
- (D) 13.4 m

45. What is the area of a circle with a circumference of 16π?

- (A) 16π
- (B) 64π
- (C) 128π
- (D) 256π

46. Find the surface area of the regular right prism.

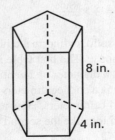

- (A) 187 in.^{2}
- (B) 105 in.^{2}
- (C) 160 in.^{2}
- (D) 215 in.^{2}

47. Find the lateral area of the right prism shown.

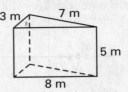

- (A) 74 m^2
- (B) 105 m^2
- (C) 85 m^2
- (D) 90 m^2

48. Find the area of the inscribed regular pentagon below. Round to the nearest tenth.

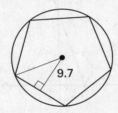

- (A) 422.3 units^2
- (B) 341.8 units^2
- (C) 211.1 units^2
- (D) 688.7 units^2

49. What is the area of the rectangle?

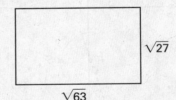

- (A) $3\sqrt{3}$
- (B) $3\sqrt{21}$
- (C) 21
- (D) $9\sqrt{21}$

50. The diagram of a roof is shown below. What is the surface area of the roof, including the underside? (slant height = 14.87 feet)

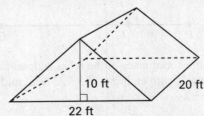

- (A) 814.8 ft^2
- (B) 1200 ft^2
- (C) 1064.54 ft^2
- (D) 1254.8 ft^2

California Standards
Pretest *continued*

51. The Jenkins family has a swimming pool in the back yard. The pool is surrounded by a 4-foot walkway. A fence encloses the pool and walkway. What is the area of the pool and walkway?

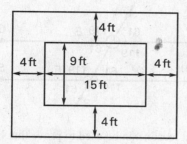

(A) 135 ft² (B) 256 ft²

(C) 64 ft² (D) 391 ft²

52. Quadrilateral *KQRA* has interior angles as shown. What is the value of *x*?

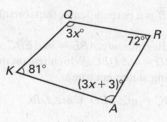

(A) 34 (B) 65

(C) 28 (D) 20

53. The sum of the perimeters of the pentagon and hexagon is 33. If the length of a side of the hexagon is equal to the length of a side of the pentagon, what is the length of a side of each polygon?

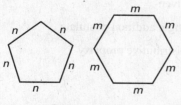

(A) 1 (B) 2 (C) 3 (D) 4

54. A square has a diagonal with length $9\sqrt{2}$. What is the length of a side of the square?

(A) 18 (B) $9\sqrt{2}$ (C) 9 (D) $\sqrt{2}$

55. A convex pentagon has exterior angles that measure 75°, 62°, 68°, and 81°. What is the measure of the exterior angle of the 5th vertex?

(A) 64° (B) 74° (C) 78° (D) 84°

56. A triangle has angles measuring $x°$, $(2x - 5)°$, and $(x + 25)°$. What is the measure of the exterior angle adjacent to the angle measuring $x°$?

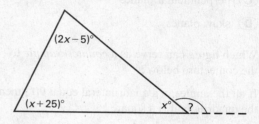

(A) 75° (B) 105° (C) 115° (D) 140°

57. Which postulate or theorem can be used to prove that $\angle HJL \cong \angle KJL$?

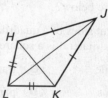

(A) SSS (B) SAS (C) ASA (D) AAS

58. Which of the following best describes inductive reasoning?

(A) inferring a general truth by examining a number of specific examples

(B) using logic to draw conclusions based on accepted statements

(C) accepting the meaning of a term without definition

(D) defining mathematical terms to correspond with physical objects

59. Which of the following is a counterexample to the conjecture "If an angle is not an acute angle, then it is obtuse"?

(A) $m\angle A = 45°$ (B) $m\angle A = 90°$

(C) $m\angle A = 135°$ (D) $m\angle A = 170°$

California Standards Pretest

California Standards
Pretest *continued*

60. "Two planes in space always intersect in exactly one line."

Which of the following best describes a *counterexample* to the assertion above?

(A) intersecting planes

(B) parallel planes

(C) perpendicular planes

(D) skew planes

61. Which figure can serve as a *counterexample* to the conjecture below?

If all the angles in a quadrilateral equal 90°, then the quadrilateral is a square.

(A) rhombus   (B) rectangle

(C) kite   (D) trapezoid

62. Which figure can serve as a *counterexample* to the conjecture below?

If the adjacent sides of a quadrilateral are equal, then the quadrilateral is a square.

(A) rectangle   (B) trapezoid

(C) rhombus   (D) parallelogram

63. Theorem: A right triangle cannot have an obtuse angle.

Joann is proving the theorem above by contradiction. She began assuming that in $\triangle ABC$, $\angle A = 90°$ and $\angle B = 91°$. Which theorem will Joann use to reach a contradiction?

(A) The sum of the measures of the angles of a triangle is 180°.

(B) The largest angle of a triangle is opposite the longest side.

(C) If two angles of a triangle are equal, the sides opposite the angles are equal.

(D) If two supplementary angles are equal, the angles each measure 90°.

64. Use the diagram to answer the question below.

$\angle PEA \cong \angle RFE$
Prove that line *PQ* is parallel to line *RS*.

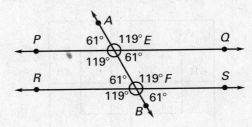

What reason can be used to prove that lines *PQ* and *RS* are parallel?

(A) The distance between $\overleftrightarrow{PQ}$ and $\overleftrightarrow{RS}$ is the same.

(B) Corresponding angles are equal.

(C) Supplementary angles are equal.

(D) $\overleftrightarrow{AB}$ is a perpendicular transversal.

65. In the diagram, $m\angle ABE = m\angle EBC$ and $m\angle EBD = m\angle DBC$. Which reason makes the following statement true?

$$m\angle EBC = m\angle EBD + m\angle DBC$$

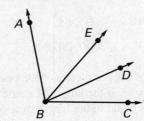

(A) substitution property

(B) given

(C) angle addition postulate

(D) distributive property

California Standards
Geometry 1.0

Undefined Terms and Reasoning

Example   **Use Inductive Reasoning**

Make a conjecture about the number of dots in the next figure in the pattern. Then sketch the next figure.

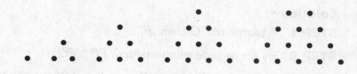

Solution

Notice that each figure is formed by adding another row of dots.

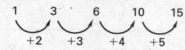

The first number increases by 2, the second number increases by 3, the third number increases by 4, and the fourth number increases by 5.

Answer Conjecture: The next number will increase by 6. There will be 21 dots in the pattern.

Exercises

1. Look for the pattern in the figures shown below. How many squares will there be in the ninth figure?

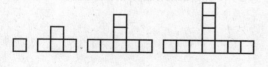

(A) 22   (B) 24   (C) 25   (D) 27

2. Which of the following is *not* used in deductive reasoning to form a logical argument?

(A) definitions

(B) facts

(C) accepted properties

(D) specific examples

3. Consider the arguments below.

I. The number pattern 1, 3, 5, 7, 9, 11, 13, 15, . . . continues forever. The number 599 is in the pattern.

II. A quadrilateral is a rhombus if and only if it has four congruent sides. Quadrilateral *ABCD* has four congruent sides, therefore quadrilateral *ABCD* is a rhombus.

Which one(s), if any, use deductive reasoning?

(A) I only

(B) II only

(C) both I and II

(D) neither I nor II

California Standards
Intensive Review

California Standards
Geometry 2.0

Geometric Proofs

Example   ### Write a Proof by Contradiction

GIVEN ▶ $\triangle PQR$ with side lengths 10, 14, and 16.

PROVE ▶ $m\angle Q < m\angle R$

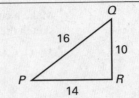

Solution

STEP 1   Assume $m\angle Q \geq m\angle R$.

STEP 2   By angle-side relationships, $PR \geq PQ$.

STEP 3   This contradicts the given side lengths, so the assumption $m\angle Q \geq m\angle R$ must be false. Therefore, $m\angle Q < m\angle R$.

Exercises

1. Use the proof to answer the question below.

Given ▶ $\overline{AB} \parallel \overline{DC}$ and $\overline{AB} \cong \overline{DC}$.
Prove ▶ $\triangle ABC \cong \triangle CDA$

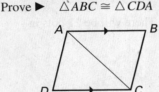

Statement	Reason
1. $\overline{AB} \parallel \overline{DC}$, $\overline{AB} \cong \overline{DC}$	1. Given
2. $\angle BAC \cong \angle DCA$	2. Alternate Interior Angles Theorem
3. $\overline{AC} \cong \overline{AC}$	3. Reflexive Property of Congruence
4. $\triangle ABC \cong \triangle CDA$	4. ?

Which reason can be used to justify Statement 4?

(A) SAS Similarity Theorem

(B) SSS Similarity Theorem

(C) SAS Congruence Postulate

(D) SSS Congruence Postulate

2. You are asked to prove the following by contradiction.

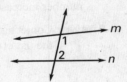

Given ▶ $m\angle 1 + m\angle 2 \neq 180°$
Prove ▶ $m \parallel n$

Which theorem or postulate will you use to reach a contradiction?

(A) Consecutive Interior Angles Converse

(B) Alternate Interior Angles Converse

(C) Congruent Complements Theorem

(D) Congruent Supplements Theorem

California Standards
Intensive Review

California Standards
Geometry 3.0

Conditional Statements and Counterexamples

Example

Analyze Conditional Statements

Write the if-then form, the converse, the inverse, and the contrapositive of the conditional statement. Decide whether each statement is *true* or *false*. For false statements, provide a counterexample.

A kite's diagonals are perpendicular.

Solution

If-then form: *If a figure is a kite, then its diagonals are perpendicular.*

A kite has perpendicular diagonals. The statement is true.

Converse: Exchange the hypothesis and the conclusion.
If a figure's diagonals are perpendicular, then it is a kite.

Counterexample: A rhombus has diagonals that are perpendicular, but a rhombus is not a kite. The statement is false.

Inverse: Negate both the hypothesis and the conclusion.
If a figure is not a kite, then its diagonals are not perpendicular.

Counterexample: A square is not a kite, but its diagonals are perpendicular. The statement is false.

Contrapositive: Write the converse.
If a figure's diagonals are perpendicular, then it is a kite.
Negate both the hypothesis and the conclusion.
If a figure's diagonals are not perpendicular, then it is not a kite.

If a figure does not have perpendicular diagonals, then it can't be a kite. The statement is true.

Exercises

1. Which statement has the same meaning as the given statement?

   > You can drive alone once you have your driver's license.

   (A) If you can drive alone, then you do have your driver's license.

   (B) If you can't drive alone, then you don't have your driver's license.

   (C) If you do have your driver's license, then you can't drive alone.

   (D) If you don't have your driver's license, then you can't drive alone.

2. *Angle 1 and angle 2 are adjacent angles; therefore, angle 1 and angle 2 form a linear pair.*
   Which of the following best describes a *counterexample* to the assertion above?

   (A) ∠1 and ∠2 each measure 60°.

   (B) ∠1 measures 60°, and ∠2 measures 120°.

   (C) ∠1 and ∠2 each measure 90°.

   (D) The measures of ∠1 and ∠2 add up to 180°.

California Standards
Intensive Review

California Standards
Geometry 1.0, 2.0, and 3.0

Mixed Review

1. What is the next number in the pattern below?

   $1, \dfrac{1}{3}, \dfrac{1}{9}, \dfrac{1}{27}, \dfrac{1}{81}, \ldots$

   (A) $\dfrac{1}{100}$ (B) $\dfrac{1}{162}$

   (C) $\dfrac{1}{243}$ (D) $\dfrac{1}{729}$

2. Identify the statement that has the same meaning as the given statement.

   The library opens at 9:00 A.M. on Thursdays.

   (A) If it is not Thursday, the library does not open at 9:00 A.M.

   (B) If it is Thursday, the library opens at 9:00 A.M.

   (C) If the library opens at 9:00 A.M., it is Thursday.

   (D) If the library does not open at 9:00 A.M., it is Thursday.

3. In the figure below, $\triangle RST$ has side lengths 4, 6, and 7.

   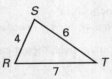

   If we assume that $m\angle T \geq m\angle R$, then we can conclude that $SR \geq ST$ by side-angle relationships. This contradicts the given triangle with $SR = 4$ and $ST = 6$. What conclusion can be drawn from this contradiction?

   (A) $m\angle T < m\angle R$ (B) $m\angle T = m\angle R$

   (C) $SR < ST$ (D) $SR \neq ST$

4. Which of the following is used in inductive reasoning to make a conjecture?

   (A) definitions

   (B) patterns

   (C) accepted properties

   (D) facts

5. A conditional statement is shown below.

   > If $\angle 1$ and $\angle 2$ are supplementary, then they form a linear pair.

   Which of the following is a counterexample to the statement?

   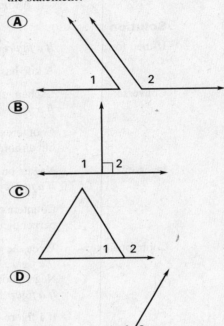

6. Consider the arguments below.

   I. The number pattern 4, 8, 12, 16, 20, 24, 28, 32, . . . continues forever. The number 198 is *not* in the pattern.

   II. The next figure in the pattern

   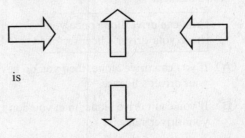

   is

   Which one(s), if any, use deductive reasoning?

   (A) only   (B) I only

   (C) both I and II   (D) neither I nor II

7. In the figure below, $m \parallel n$.

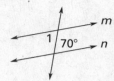

Identify the postulate or theorem that proves the statement $m\angle 1 = 70°$.

(A) Corresponding Angles Postulate

(B) Alternate Interior Angles Theorem

(C) Alternate Exterior Angles Theorem

(D) Consecutive Interior Angles Theorem

8. You are told that a conditional statement is true. Consider the related conditionals.

I. Inverse

II. Contrapositive

III. Converse

Which one(s) are false?

(A) I only

(B) II only

(C) III only

(D) both I and III

9. Marcus wants to prove that there can be no more than one obtuse angle in a triangle. What assumption should he make to write a proof by contradiction?

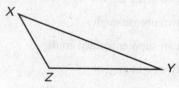

(A) $\angle X$ is obtuse.

(B) $\angle Z$ is obtuse.

(C) $\angle X$ and $\angle Z$ are obtuse.

(D) $\angle X$, $\angle Y$, and $\angle Z$ are obtuse.

10. Given ▶ $DE \neq EF$, $EF \neq FD$, $FD \neq DE$

Prove ▶ $\triangle DEF$ is scalene.

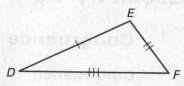

Consider the two assumptions.

I. $\triangle DEF$ is isosceles.

II. $\triangle DEF$ is equilateral.

Which one(s), if any, would you use to write a proof by contradiction?

(A) I only

(B) II only

(C) both I and II

(D) neither I nor II

11. Which of the following represents an undefined term?

(A) A ●——————————▶

(B)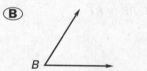

B

(C) ◀————▶——— m

◀————▶——— n

(D) ● D

12. *"If two polygons have the same area, then they are congruent."*

Which of the following best describes a counterexample to the assertion above?

(A) two similar circles

(B) two similar triangles

(C) a 2 meter by 8 meter rectangle and a 4 meter by 4 meter square

(D) a 2 meter by 2 meter square and a 4 meter by 4 meter square

California Standards
Intensive Review

California Standards
Geometry 4.0

Congruence and Similarity

Example

Congruence

GIVEN ▶ $\overline{PQ} \cong \overline{ST}$. R is the midpoint of $\overline{QS}$.

PROVE ▶ $\overline{PR} \cong \overline{RT}$

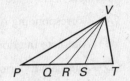

Solution

Statements	Reasons
1. $\overline{PQ} \cong \overline{ST}$ R is the midpoint of $\overline{QS}$.	1. Given
2. $QR = RS$	2. Definition of midpoint
3. $PQ = ST$	3. Definition of congruent segments
4. $PQ + QR = RS + ST$	4. Addition Property
5. $PQ + QR = PR$ $RS + ST = RT$	5. Segment Addition Postulate
6. $PR = RT$	6. Substitution
7. $\overline{PR} \cong \overline{RT}$	7. Definition of congruent segments

Exercises

1. In the diagram, $\triangle ABC \sim \triangle DEF$. What is the value of x?

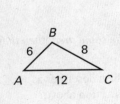

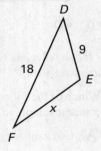

Ⓐ $5\frac{1}{3}$

Ⓑ 6

Ⓒ 12

Ⓓ $13\frac{1}{2}$

2. Determine which pair of angles must be congruent.

Ⓐ two acute angles

Ⓑ two obtuse angles

Ⓒ two supplementary angles

Ⓓ two right angles

California Standards
Geometry 5.0

Triangle Congruence and Similarity

Example   **Determine Whether Triangles are Congruent or Similar**

Decide whether the statement is true. Explain your reasoning.

a. $\triangle DEG \cong \triangle FEG$

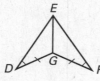

b. $\triangle JPK \cong \triangle LPM$

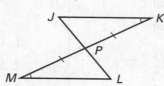

c. $\triangle ACE \sim \triangle BCD$

Solution

a. No, the information given is SSA, which is not one of the triangle congruence postulates or theorems.

b. Yes, by the ASA Congruence Theorem. $\angle JPK \cong \angle LPM$ by the Vertical Angles Congruence Theorem. $\angle K \cong \angle M$ and $\overline{PK} \cong \overline{PM}$ are given.

c. Yes, by the SAS Similarity Theorem. $\angle C \cong \angle C$ by the Reflexive Property of Congruent Angles. $AC = AB + BC$ and $EC = ED + DC$ by the Segment Addition Postulate. $BC = DC$ and $AB = ED$ are given. $AC = EC$ by substitution. $\frac{BC}{AC} = \frac{DC}{EC}$ by the Division Property. The lengths of the sides including the congruent angle are proportional.

Exercises

1. In the figure below, $\overline{BC} \parallel \overline{AD}$.

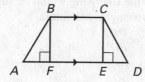

Which additional information would be enough to prove $\triangle ABF \cong \triangle DCE$?

(A) $\overline{AB} \cong \overline{BC}$ **(B)** $\overline{AE} \cong \overline{FD}$

(C) $\overline{BC} \cong \overline{EF}$ **(D)** $\overline{BF} \cong \overline{CE}$

2. In the figure below, $\overline{SQ}$ is an altitude to $\triangle PSR$.

Which theorem or postulate can be used to prove $\triangle PRS \sim \triangle SRQ$?

(A) HL   **(B)** SSS

(C) SAS   **(D)** AA

California Standards Intensive Review

California Standards
Geometry 4.0 and 5.0

Mixed Review

1. In the figure below, $\angle 2 \cong \angle 5$.

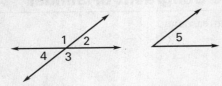

Which pair of angles must be supplementary?

  (A) $\angle 1$ and $\angle 3$ **(B)** $\angle 3$ and $\angle 5$

  (C) $\angle 2$ and $\angle 4$ **(D)** $\angle 2$ and $\angle 5$

2. In the figure below, $\angle P \cong \angle U$, $\angle Q \cong \angle T$, and $\overline{QR} \cong \overline{ST}$.

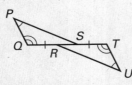

Which theorem or postulate can be used to prove $\triangle PQS \cong \triangle UTR$?

  (A) AAS   **(B)** SSS

  (C) SAS   **(D)** ASA

3. In the diagram, $\triangle PQR \sim \triangle STU$. What is the value of x?

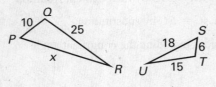

  (A) 45   **(B)** 35

  (C) 30   **(D)** 20

4. All of the triangles in the figure are similar. $JK = 20$ and $KL = 15$.

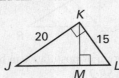

What is the length of $\overline{KM}$?

  (A) 9   **(B)** 12

  (C) 16   **(D)** 18

5. Use the proof to answer the question below.

  Given ▶ $AE = BE$, $ED = EC$
  Prove ▶ $AC = BD$

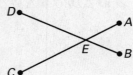

Statement	Reason
1. $AE = BE$, $ED = EC$	1. Given
2. $AE + EC = BE + EC$	2. Addition Property
3. $AE + EC = BE + ED$	3. Substitution
4. $AE + EC = AC$, $BE + ED = BD$	4. ?
5. $AC = BD$	5. Substitution

Which reason can be used to justify Statement 4?

  (A) Segment Addition Postulate

  (B) Reflexive Property of Segment Congruence

  (C) Symmetric Property of Segment Congruence

  (D) Transitive Property of Segment Congruence

6. In the figure below, $\overline{DE} \parallel \overline{GF}$.

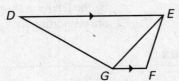

Which of the following would be sufficient to prove the triangles are similar?

  (A) $\dfrac{DG}{DE} = \dfrac{GF}{EG}$

  (B) $\dfrac{EG}{EF} = \dfrac{DE}{DG}$

  (C) $\dfrac{DE}{EG} = \dfrac{EG}{GF}$

  (D) $\dfrac{DG}{EF} = \dfrac{EG}{GF}$

California Standards
Intensive Review

7. In the figure below, $m\angle BGD = 90°$.

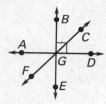

Which pair of angles can be proven congruent?

Ⓐ ∠AGC, ∠CGE

Ⓑ ∠CGD, ∠FGE

Ⓒ ∠BGC, ∠AFG

Ⓓ ∠BGF, ∠CGE

8. In the figure below, quadrilateral $PQRS$ is a square and $RT = RU$.

Which theorem or postulate can be used to prove $\triangle RST \cong \triangle RQU$?

Ⓐ SSS

Ⓑ AAS

Ⓒ SAS

Ⓓ HL

9. Which statement about the figure is *not* true?

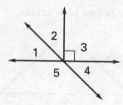

Ⓐ ∠2 and ∠4 are congruent angles.

Ⓑ ∠1 and ∠2 are complementary angles.

Ⓒ ∠1 and ∠4 are vertical angles.

Ⓓ ∠1 and ∠5 are supplementary angles.

10. In the figure below, C is the midpoint of $\overline{AD}$.

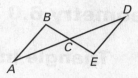

Which additional piece of information is needed to prove $\triangle ABC \cong \triangle DEC$?

Ⓐ $\overline{AC} \cong \overline{CD}$

Ⓑ $\overline{AB} \parallel \overline{DE}$

Ⓒ $\angle BCA \cong \angle ECD$

Ⓓ $\overline{AB} \cong \overline{DE}$

11. In the figure, $PQRS \sim WXYZ$. Which statement must be true?

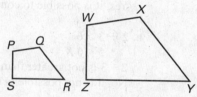

Ⓐ The corresponding side lengths of the two quadrilaterals are equal.

Ⓑ The corresponding angles of the two quadrilaterals are congruent.

Ⓒ The perimeters of the two quadrilaterals are equal.

Ⓓ The areas of the two quadrilaterals are equal.

12. $\triangle JKL$ and $\triangle PQR$ are two triangles such that $\angle J \cong \angle P$. Which of the following is sufficient to prove the triangles are similar?

Ⓐ $\dfrac{JK}{KL} = \dfrac{PQ}{QR}$

Ⓑ $\dfrac{JL}{PR} = \dfrac{KL}{QR}$

Ⓒ $\dfrac{JL}{KL} = \dfrac{PR}{PQ}$

Ⓓ $\dfrac{JK}{PQ} = \dfrac{JL}{PR}$

California Standards
Geometry 6.0

Triangle Inequality Theorem

Example   **Use the Triangle Inequality Theorem**

Is it possible to construct a triangle with the given side lengths? If not, explain why not.

a. 6, 8, 11

b. 2, 3, 6

c. 4, 5, 8

Solution

a. $6 + 8 \overset{?}{>} 11$ $6 + 11 \overset{?}{>} 8$ $8 + 11 \overset{?}{>} 6$
$14 > 11$ ✓ $17 > 8$ ✓ $19 > 6$ ✓

Yes, it is possible to construct a triangle with these side lengths.

b. $2 + 3 \overset{?}{>} 6$
$5 < 6$ ✗
$2 + 3$ is not greater than 6.
No, it is not possible to construct a triangle with these side lengths.

c. $4 + 5 \overset{?}{>} 8$ $4 + 8 \overset{?}{>} 5$ $5 + 8 \overset{?}{>} 4$
$9 > 8$ ✓ $12 > 5$ ✓ $13 > 4$ ✓

Yes, it is possible to construct a triangle with these side lengths.

Exercises

1. The lengths of two sides of the triangle are known.

Which of the following could be the perimeter of the triangle?

(A) 22   (B) 26

(C) 28   (D) 36

2. A triangle has one side of length 16 and another of length 25. Which of the following *best* describes the possible lengths of the third side?

(A) $16 < x < 34$

(B) $16 < x < 25$

(C) $9 < x < 16$

(D) $9 < x < 41$

3. The triangle below is isosceles.

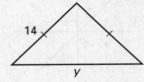

If *y* is a whole number, what is its *largest* possible value?

(A) 26

(B) 27

(C) 28

(D) 29

California Standards
Geometry 7.0

Parallel Lines, Quadrilaterals, and Circles

Example 1   ### Prove a Quadrilateral is a Parallelogram

GIVEN ▶ E is the midpoint of $\overline{BD}$.
      $\angle BAE \cong \angle DCE$
PROVE ▶ $ABCD$ is a parallelogram.

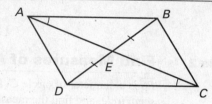

Solution

Statements	Reasons
1. E is the midpoint of $\overline{BD}$. $\angle BAE \cong \angle DCE$	1. Given
2. $\overline{DE} \cong \overline{EB}$	2. Definition of midpoint
3. $\angle AEB \cong \angle CED$	3. Vertical Angles Congruence Theorem
4. $\triangle AEB \cong \triangle CED$	4. AAS Congruence Theorem
5. $\overline{AB} \cong \overline{CD}$	5. Corresponding parts of congruent triangles are congruent.
6. $\overline{AB} \parallel \overline{CD}$	6. Alternate Interior Angles Converse
7. $ABCD$ is a parallelogram.	7. If one pair of opposite sides of a quadrilateral are congruent and parallel, then the quadrilateral is a parallelogram.

Exercises

1. Identify the postulate or theorem that justifies the statement about the diagram.

   $\angle 4$ and $\angle 6$ are supplementary angles.

   Ⓐ Corresponding Angles Postulate

   Ⓑ Alternate Exterior Angles Theorem

   Ⓒ Alternate Interior Angles Theorem

   Ⓓ Consecutive Interior Angles Theorem

2. Quadrilateral $WXYZ$ is a parallelogram. If its diagonals are congruent, which statement must be true?

   Ⓐ Quadrilateral $WXYZ$ is a kite.

   Ⓑ Quadrilateral $WXYZ$ is a rhombus.

   Ⓒ Quadrilateral $WXYZ$ is a rectangle.

   Ⓓ Quadrilateral $WXYZ$ is an isosceles trapezoid.

3. What is the value of z in the diagram?

(A) 7   (B) 14   (C) 56   (D) 70

4. Quadrilateral $PQRS$ is a trapezoid.

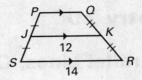

What is PQ?

(A) 8   (B) 10   (C) 13   (D) 16

Example 2

Find Measures of Arcs

$\overline{PS}$ is a diameter of circle C. Identify the given arc as a *major arc, minor arc,* or *semicircle,* and find the measure of the arc.

   a. $\widehat{PQS}$ **b.** $\widehat{PR}$

   c. $\widehat{QR}$ **d.** $\widehat{RSP}$

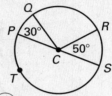

Solution

a. $m\angle PQS = 180°$

   $m\widehat{PQS}$ is 180°. It is a semicircle.

b. $m\widehat{PR} = m\widehat{PQS} - m\widehat{RS}$

   $= 180° - 50°$

   $= 130°$

   $m\widehat{PR}$ is less than 180°. It is a minor arc.

c. $m\widehat{QR} = m\widehat{PQS} - m\widehat{PQ} - m\widehat{RS}$

   $= 180° - 30° - 50°$

   $= 100°$

   $m\widehat{QR}$ is less than 180°. It is a minor arc.

d. $m\widehat{RSP} = m\widehat{RS} + m\widehat{STP}$

   $= 50° + 180°$

   $= 230°$

   $m\widehat{RSP}$ is greater than 180°. It is a major arc.

Exercises

1. $\overline{PQ}$ and $\overline{MN}$ are diameters of circle C.

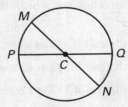

If $m\widehat{QN} = 45°$, what is $m\widehat{PQN}$?

(A) 45°   (B) 135°   (C) 180°   (D) 225°

2. In the figure at the right, $m\widehat{AB} = 120°$ and $BC = 9$. What is the diameter of circle P?

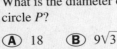

(A) 18   (B) $9\sqrt{3}$

(C) $9\sqrt{2}$ (D) 9

3. In the figure below, $\overline{AC}$ is a diameter of circle X, and $\overline{GJ}$ is a diameter of circle Y. Which statement is true?

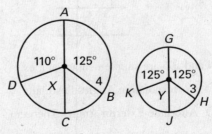

(A) $\widehat{GH} \cong \widehat{BCD}$ (B) $\widehat{AB} \cong \widehat{GK}$

(C) $\widehat{AB} \cong \widehat{BCD}$ (D) $\widehat{GK} \cong \widehat{KJH}$

4. In circle P, $m\widehat{AB} = 60°$ and $m\widehat{BC} = 35°$. Which of the following is *not* a possible measure of $\widehat{AC}$?

(A) 25°   (B) 85°   (C) 265°   (D) 335°

Name _____   Date _____

California Standard
Geometry 6.0 and 7.0

Mixed Review

1. Which of the following sets of numbers could *not* represent the lengths of the sides of a triangle?

  (A) 3, 9, 14   (B) 6, 8, 12

  (C) 15, 20, 30   (D) 11, 11, 19

2. Use the proof to answer the question below.

Given ▶ $p \parallel q$

Prove ▶ ∠2 is supplementary to ∠3.

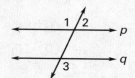

Statement	**Reason**
1. $p \parallel q$	1. Given
2. ∠2 and ∠1 are a linear pair.	2. Definition of linear pair
3. ∠2 is supplementary to ∠1.	3. Linear Pair Postulate
4. ∠1 ≅ ∠3	4. ?
5. ∠2 is supplementary to ∠3.	5. Congruent Supplements Theorem

What reason can be used to justify Statement 4?

  (A) Vertical Angles Congruence Theorem

  (B) Alternate Interior Angles Theorem

  (C) Alternate Exterior Angles Theorem

  (D) Consecutive Interior Angles Theorem

3. In circle C, $m\overset{\frown}{PQ} = 35°$ and $m\overset{\frown}{QR} = 50°$. Which of the following is *not* a possible measure of $\overset{\frown}{PR}$?

  (A) 15°   (B) 95°   (C) 275°   (D) 345°

4. Two sides of a triangle measure 11 and 4. Which of the following could be the perimeter of the triangle?

  (A) 20   (B) 22

  (C) 28   (D) 30

5. A triangle has one side of length 20 and another of length 10. Which of the following best describes the possible lengths of the third side?

  (A) $10 < x < 20$ (B) $11 < x < 29$

  (C) $20 < x < 30$ (D) $10 < x < 30$

6. The figure shows the outline of a sign for a shopping center.

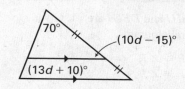

Which of the following is a possible measure for the third side of the sign?

  (A) 2 ft   (B) 3 ft

  (C) 4 ft   (D) 5 ft

7. What is the value of d in the diagram?

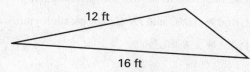

  (A) 5   (B) 10   (C) 35   (D) 75

8. Quadrilateral $JKLM$ is a parallelogram. If it has four right angles and its diagonals are perpendicular, which statement must be true?

  (A) Quadrilateral $JKLM$ is a kite.

  (B) Quadrilateral $JKLM$ is a rhombus.

  (C) Quadrilateral $JKLM$ is a rectangle.

  (D) Quadrilateral $JKLM$ is a square.

9. Quadrilateral $PQRS$ is a kite. What is $m\angle R$?

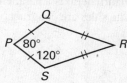

  (A) 40°   (B) 60°   (C) 120°   (D) 160°

10. Identify the postulate or theorem that justifies the statement about the diagram.

$\angle 4 \cong \angle 5$

- **Ⓐ** Corresponding Angles Postulate
- **Ⓑ** Alternate Exterior Angles Theorem
- **Ⓒ** Alternate Interior Angles Theorem
- **Ⓓ** Consecutive Interior Angles Theorem

11. Use the proof to answer the question below.

Given ▶ *ABHJ* and *DFGJ* are parallelograms

Prove ▶ $\angle B \cong \angle F$

Statement	**Reason**
1. *ABHJ* and *DFGJ* are parallelograms.	1. Given
2. $\angle B \cong \angle J$, $\angle F \cong \angle J$	2. ?
3. $\angle B \cong \angle F$	3. Transitive Property of Angle Congruence

What reason can be used to justify Statement 2?

- **Ⓐ** If a quadrilateral is a parallelogram, then its opposite angles are congruent.
- **Ⓑ** If a quadrilateral is a parallelogram, then its diagonals bisect each other.
- **Ⓒ** If a quadrilateral is a parallelogram, then its consecutive angles are supplementary.
- **Ⓓ** If a quadrilateral is a parallelogram, then its opposite sides are congruent.

12. Quadrilateral *ABCD* is a trapezoid. What is *AB*?

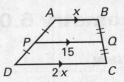

- **Ⓐ** 5
- **Ⓑ** 10
- **Ⓒ** 20
- **Ⓓ** 30

13. $\overline{JK}$ and $\overline{ST}$ are diameters of circle *A* in the figure. If $m\overset{\frown}{SK} = 42°$, what is $m\overset{\frown}{KST}$?

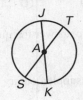

- **Ⓐ** 42°
- **Ⓑ** 84°
- **Ⓒ** 222°
- **Ⓓ** 276°

14. In the figure below, $\overline{XZ}$ is a diameter of circle *C* and *XZ* = 6.

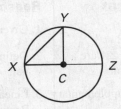

If $m\overset{\frown}{YZ} = 90°$, what is *XY*?

- **Ⓐ** $6\sqrt{2}$
- **Ⓑ** $3\sqrt{3}$
- **Ⓒ** $3\sqrt{2}$
- **Ⓓ** 3

15. In the figure below, *PQRS* is a parallelogram. What are the values of *a* and *b*?

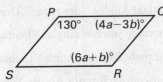

- **Ⓐ** $a = 10, b = 20$
- **Ⓑ** $a = 20, b = 10$
- **Ⓒ** $a = 50, b = 130$
- **Ⓓ** $a = 130, b = 50$

California Standards
Geometry 8.0, 9.0

Perimeter, Area, and Volume

Example 1   **Find Perimeter, Lateral Area and Volume**

The figure shows a model of an office building that has the shape of a rectangular prism with an open courtyard in the center of the building.

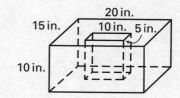

a. Find the outside perimeter of the model.

b. Find the area of the outer walls of the model.

c. Find the volume of the model.

Solution

a. $P = 2\ell + 2w = 2(20) + 2(15) = 40 + 30 = 70$ in.

b. The area of the outer walls is the sum of the area of the front, back, and sides. The front and back have the same area, and the sides have the same area.

$$A = 2(\ell_{front} \cdot h_{front}) + 2(\ell_{side} \cdot h_{side})$$ **Write formula.**
$$= 2(20)(10) + 2(15)(10)$$ **Substitute.**
$$= 700 \text{ in.}^2$$ **Simplify.**

c. To find the volume, subtract the volume of the courtyard, or hole, from the volume of the outer prism.

$$V = B_{prism} \cdot h_{prism} - B_{hole} \cdot h_{hole}$$ **Write formula.**
$$= 20(15)(10) - 10(5)(15)$$ **Substitute.**
$$= 3000 - 750$$ **Simplify.**
$$= 2250 \text{ in.}^3$$ **Simplify.**

Exercises

1. A storage shed is shown below. What is the combined area of the sides and top of the shed?

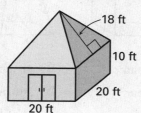

Ⓐ 1520 ft²   Ⓑ 1860 ft²

Ⓒ 2240 ft²   Ⓓ 2440 ft²

2. Nick jogs once around the triangular path shown. About how far does he jog?

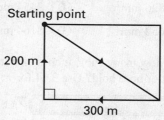

Ⓐ 522.4 m   Ⓑ 860.6 m

Ⓒ 980.5 m   Ⓓ 1221.1 m

California Standards
Intensive Review

Name _____   Date _____

Example 2

Find Volume and Surface Area

A candle in the shape of a right cone is shown in the figure.

a. Find the surface area of the candle.

b. Find the volume of the wax needed to make the candle.

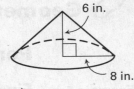

Solution

a. STEP 1 Find the slant height ℓ of the candle.

$\ell^2 = h^2 + r^2$	**Use Pythagorean Theorem.**
$\ell^2 = 6^2 + 8^2$	**Substitute.**
$\ell^2 = 100$	**Simplify.**
$\ell = 10$	**Find positive square root.**

STEP 2 Find the surface area of the candle.

$S = \pi r^2 + \pi r \ell$	**Formula for surface area of right cone.**
$= \pi(8^2) + \pi(8)(10)$	**Substitute.**
$= 144\pi \approx 452.16$	**Simplify. Use 3.14 for π.**

The surface area of the candle is about 452.16 square inches.

b.

$v = \frac{1}{3}(\pi r^2)h$	**Write formula.**
$= \frac{1}{3}\pi(8^2)6$	**Substitute.**
$= 128\pi \approx 401.92$	**Simplify. Use 3.14 for π.**

The volume of wax needed to make the candle is about 401.92 cubic inches.

Exercises

1. A diagram of a cylinder is shown below. What is the total surface area of the cylinder in square millimeters? Use 3.14 for π.

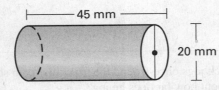

   A 2826 mm²   **B** 3454 mm²

   C 5652 mm²   **D** 8164 mm²

2. About how many cubic inches of water can 10 feet of hose hold? Use 3.14 for π.

   A 18 in.³   **B** 212 in.³

   C 848 in.³   **D** 1507 in.³

3. A rectangular prism and a pyramid have the dimensions shown. If the volume of the prism is 96 cubic millimeters, what is the volume of the pyramid?

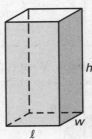 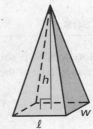

   A 32 mm³   **B** 48 mm³

   C 96 mm³   **D** 288 mm³

California Standards
Geometry 10.0

Area

Example 1   **Find Area**

The height of a triangle is 17.5 centimeters, which is two and one half times the length of its base. Find the base and the area of the triangle.

Solution

STEP 1 Find the base of the triangle.
Let b represent the base of the triangle.

$$2.5b = 17.5$$
$$b = \frac{17.5}{2.5} = 7$$

STEP 2 Find the area of the triangle.

$$A = \frac{1}{2}bh \qquad \text{Formula for area of a triangle}$$
$$= \frac{1}{2}(7)(17.5) \quad \text{Substitute.}$$
$$= 61.25 \qquad \text{Simplify.}$$

Answer The base of the triangle is 7 centimeters, and the area of the triangle is 61.25 square centimeters.

Exercises

1. A crosswalk at an intersection is shaped like a parallelogram. What is the area enclosed by the crosswalk?

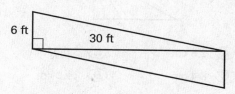

6 ft

30 ft

(A) 72 ft²   (B) 90 ft²
(C) 180 ft²   (D) 360 ft²

2. What is the area of the triangle shown below?

4

(A) $4\sqrt{2}$ (B) $4\sqrt{3}$
(C) $16\sqrt{2}$ (D) $16\sqrt{3}$

3. Max removes the bottom from a square crate and tilts the sides into the shape of a rhombus with one diagonal of 6 feet.

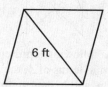

6 ft

If the area of the original crate bottom is 25 square feet, what is the area formed by the sides of the rhombus?

(A) 18 ft²
(B) 24 ft²
(C) 25 ft²
(D) 30 ft²

California Standards
Intensive Review

Example 2

Use Area

A metal CD holder has 11 openings shaped like congruent rhombi. The total area of the CD holder is 297 square inches, and the total width is 18 inches. Find the area of one rhombus, the length of each diagonal, and the total height of the CD holder. Ignore the thickness of the metal.

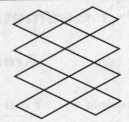

Solution

STEP 1 Find the area of each rhombus.

$$A = \frac{297 \text{ in.}^2}{11} = 27 \text{ in.}^2$$

STEP 2 Find one diagonal of each rhombus. The CD holder is two rhombi wide, so divide the total width by 2.

$$d_1 = \frac{18 \text{ in.}}{2} = 9 \text{ in.}$$

STEP 3 Find the other diagonal of each rhombus.

$$A = \frac{1}{2} d_1 d_2$$ **With formula for area of a rhombus.**

$$27 = \frac{1}{2}(9)d_2$$ **Substitute.**

$$d_2 = 6 \text{ in.}$$ **Simplify.**

STEP 4 Find the height of the CD holder. The CD holder is four rhombi high, so multiply the shorter diagonal by 4.

$$h = 4(6 \text{ in.}) = 24 \text{ in.}$$

Exercises

1. In the figure below four congruent parallelograms form part of a tile floor pattern.

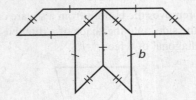

   Which of the following represents the total width of the pattern in terms of A, the area of one parallelogram, and b, the length of one base?

   A $b + \frac{A}{b}$

   B $2\left(b + \frac{2A}{b}\right)$

   C $2\left(b + \frac{b}{A}\right)$

   D $2\left(b + \frac{A}{b}\right)$

2. The triangle in the figure below has an area of 53.2 square centimeters. What is the length of $\overline{AC}$?

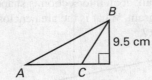

   A 2.8 cm   **B** 5.6 cm

   C 8.4 cm   **D** 11.2 cm

3. Francine arranges 4 straws on a table to form a square with an area of 169 square inches. She then rearranges the same straws to form a rhombus. If the length of one of the diagonals of the rhombus is 24 inches, what is the area of the rhombus?

   A 240 in.²   **B** 120 in.²

   C 78 in.²   **D** 60 in.²

California Standards
Geometry 11.0

Changing Dimensions

Example

Change Volume

A health food store sells a small box of mixed nuts for $5. The dimensions of a larger box are 1.2 times those of the small box. What is a reasonable price for the large box?

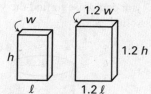

Solution

STEP 1 Find the ratio of the volumes of the two boxes.

If two similar solids have a scale factor of $a : b$, then corresponding volumes have a ratio of $a^3 : b^3$.

The scale factor of the dimensions of the large box to the small box is $1.2 : 1$, so the corresponding volumes have a ratio of $1.2^3 : 1^3 = 1.728 : 1$.

STEP 2 Find the price of the large box. Since the large box has a volume that is 1.728 times the volume of the small box, the price of the large box should be 1.728 times the price of the small box.

Price $= 1.728(5) = 8.64$

Answer A reasonable price for the large box is $8.64.

Exercises

1. A swimming pool in the shape of a rectangular prism has volume 960 cubic feet. A similar pool next door has dimensions twice as large. What is the volume of the larger pool?

　(**A**) 1920 ft³

　(**B**) 3840 ft³

　(**C**) 7680 ft³

　(**D**) 9600 ft³

2. The ratio of the diameters of two spheres is $\frac{3}{2}$.

What is the ratio of the surface area of the larger sphere to the surface area of the smaller sphere?

　(**A**) $\frac{8}{27}$

　(**B**) $\frac{4}{9}$

　(**C**) $\frac{9}{4}$

　(**D**) $\frac{27}{8}$

3. The ratio of the side lengths of $\triangle WXY$ to the corresponding side lengths of $\triangle LMN$ is 1 to 4. What is the perimeter of $\triangle LMN$?

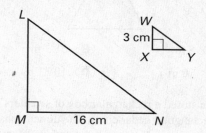

　(**A**) 12 cm

　(**B**) 23 cm

　(**C**) 33 cm

　(**D**) 48 cm

California Standards
Geometry 8.0, 9.0, 10.0, and 11.0

Mixed Review

1. A solid is formed by removing a cone from a cylinder, as shown below. Which equation could you could use to find the volume of the resulting solid?

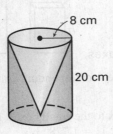

8 cm

20 cm

(A) $V = \pi \cdot 8^2 \cdot 20 - \frac{1}{3}\pi \cdot 8^2 \cdot 20$

(B) $V = 2\pi \cdot 8 \cdot 20 - \pi \cdot 8 \cdot 21 \cdot 5$

(C) $V = \pi \cdot 8^2 \cdot 20 + \frac{1}{3}\pi \cdot 8^2 \cdot 20$

(D) $V = \frac{1}{3}\pi \cdot 8^2 \cdot 20$

2. The area of the triangle shown below is $25\sqrt{3}$ square meters. What is the length of one side of the triangle?

(A) 5 m   (B) $5\sqrt{3}$ m

(C) 10 m   (D) $10\sqrt{3}$ m

3. Erin stored a rectangular box of sweaters inside a rectangular cedar chest. The dimensions of the box and chest are shown below. What is the volume of the empty space in the cedar chest?

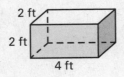 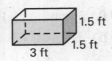

2 ft

2 ft

4 ft

1.5 ft

1.5 ft

3 ft

(A) 0.25 ft³

(B) 3 ft³

(C) 6.75 ft³

(D) 9.25 ft³

4. A silo is used to store food for livestock on a farm. The shape of the silo is a cylinder with a hemisphere on top. To the nearest cubic yard, what is the volume of the silo?

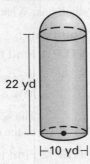

22 yd

├─10 yd─┤

(A) 9006 yd³   (B) 2775 yd³

(C) 2252 yd³   (D) 1990 yd³

5. A rectangular swimming pool is 9 meters long and 6 meters wide, and it has a flat bottom. The pool is surrounded by a brick walkway of a uniform width as shown in the figure below. If the area of the walkway is equal to the area of the bottom of the pool, what is the uniform width of the walkway?

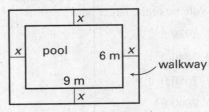

x

x   pool   6 m   x

9 m

x

walkway

(A) 1 m   (B) 1.5 m

(C) 2.25 m   (D) 3 m

6. Mrs. Cooper is buying edging for three circular gardens that have the dimensions shown below. She can purchase the edging in packages of 12 feet. How many packages of edging does Mrs. Cooper need to buy? Use 3.14 for π.

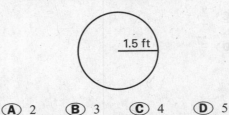

1.5 ft

(A) 2   (B) 3   (C) 4   (D) 5

7. The figure below is a trapezoid with an area of 22.5 square yards. What is the length of the longest base of the trapezoid?

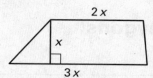

- Ⓐ 3 yd
- Ⓑ 6 yd
- Ⓒ 7.5 yd
- Ⓓ 9 yd

8. The lateral area of the cone in the diagram below is 96π square yards. The lateral area of a cone $= \pi r \ell$, where ℓ is the slant height. What is the radius of the base?

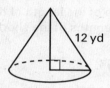

- Ⓐ 2 yd
- Ⓑ 4 yd
- Ⓒ 8 yd
- Ⓓ 16 yd

9. What is the volume of the sphere in cubic meters? Use 3.14 for π. Round your answer to the nearest whole number.

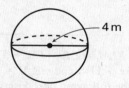

- Ⓐ 34 m³
- Ⓑ 50 m³
- Ⓒ 201 m³
- Ⓓ 268 m³

10. The triangles shown below are similar. What is the ratio of the perimeter of the larger right triangle to the perimeter of the smaller right triangle?

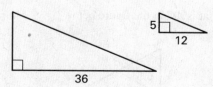

- Ⓐ 36 : 5
- Ⓑ 9 : 1
- Ⓒ 3 : 1
- Ⓓ 36 : 3

11. Two similar cones are shown below. The volume of the larger cone is 3600 cubic centimeters. What is the volume of the smaller cone?

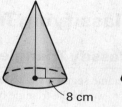

- Ⓐ 450 cm³
- Ⓑ 900 cm³
- Ⓒ 1250 cm³
- Ⓓ 1800 cm³

12. Katie is sending a map in the cylindrical tube shown below. She plans to gift wrap all but the ends of the cylinder. How many square inches of wrap does she need to the nearest square inch? Use 3.14 for π.

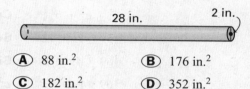

- Ⓐ 88 in.²
- Ⓑ 176 in.²
- Ⓒ 182 in.²
- Ⓓ 352 in.²

13. The figure below shows the borders of a county park. What is the area of the park?

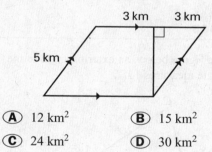

- Ⓐ 12 km²
- Ⓑ 15 km²
- Ⓒ 24 km²
- Ⓓ 30 km²

14. What is the surface area of the largest ball that will fit inside a cubical box that has a volume of 64 cubic centimeters? Round to the nearest tenth of a square centimeter. Use 3.14 for π.

- Ⓐ 25.1 cm²
- Ⓑ 50.2 cm²
- Ⓒ 200.0 cm²
- Ⓓ 803.8 cm²

California Standards
Geometry 12.0

Classifying Triangles and Polygons

Example 1   **Classify Triangles**

Can line segments with lengths of 7 inches, 12 inches, and 13 inches form a triangle? If so, would the triangle be *acute*, *right*, or *obtuse*?

Solution

STEP 1 Use the Triangle Inequality Theorem to check that the segments can make a triangle.

$$7 + 12 = 19 \qquad 7 + 13 = 20 \qquad 12 + 13 = 25$$
$$19 > 13 \qquad\quad 20 > 12 \qquad\quad 25 > 7$$

STEP 2 Classify the triangle by comparing the square of the length of the longest side with the sum of squares of the lengths of the shorter sides.

$c^2 \; \underset{?}{} \; a^2 + b^2$	**Compare c^2 with $a^2 + b^2$.**
$13^2 \; \underset{?}{} \; 7^2 + 12^2$	**Substitute.**
$169 \; \underset{?}{} \; 49 + 144$	**Simplify.**
$169 < 193$	**c^2 is less than $a^2 + b^2$.**

Answer The side lengths 7 inches, 12 inches, and 13 inches form an acute triangle.

Exercises

1. In the figure below, an exterior angle of the triangle measures 145°.

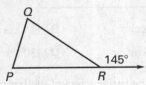

Which of the following could *not* be the measures of interior angles *P* and *Q*?

  (A) 90° and 45°   **(B)** 85° and 60°

  (C) 80° and 65°   **(D)** 75° and 70°

2. The side lengths of a triangle are 7, *x*, and 25. If the length of the longest side is 25, what are the values of *x* that make the triangle an obtuse triangle?

  (A) $18 < x < 32$ **(B)** $18 < x < 24$

  (C) $24 < x < 25$ **(D)** $18 < x < 25$

3. In triangle *KLM*, $m\angle K = (3x + 5)°$, $m\angle L = (5x - 11)°$, and $m\angle M = (8x - 6)°$. Which of the following *best* describes triangle *KLM*?

  (A) right triangle

  (B) equilateral triangle

  (C) isosceles triangle

  (D) scalene triangle

4. What is *AC* in the figure below?

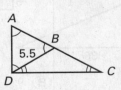

  (A) 5.5   **(B)** 10   **(C)** 11   **(D)** 12

California Standards
Intensive Review

Name _____ Date _____

Example 2 **Find Angle Measures in a Polygon**

Find the measures of the angles in the polygon.

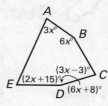

Solution

STEP 1 The polygon is a pentagon. Use the Polygon Interior Angles Theorem with $n = 5$ to write an equation involving x. Then solve the equation.

$$m\angle 1 + m\angle 2 + \cdots + m\angle n = (n - 2) \cdot 180°$$ **Write equation.**

$$m\angle A + m\angle B + m\angle C + m\angle D + m\angle E = (5 - 2) \cdot 180°$$ **Substitute.**

$$(3x)° + (6x)° + (3x - 3)° + (6x + 8)° + (2x + 15)° = 540°$$ **Substitute.**

$$20x + 20 = 540$$ **Simplify.**

$$20x = 520$$ **Subtract 20 from each side.**

$$x = 26$$ **Divide each side by 20.**

STEP 2 Use the value of x to find the measures of the angles.

$$m\angle A = 3x = 3(26) = 78°$$

$$m\angle B = 6x = 6(26) = 156°$$

$$m\angle C = 3x - 3 = 3(26) - 3 = 78 - 3 = 75°$$

$$m\angle D = 6x + 8 = 6(26) + 8 = 156 + 8 = 164°$$

$$m\angle E = 2x + 15 = 2(26) + 15 = 52 + 15 = 67°$$

Check The sum of the angles is $78° + 156° + 75° + 164° + 67° = 540°$. This sum satisfies the Polygon Interior Angles Theorem with $n = 5$.

Exercises

1. An exterior angle of a regular polygon measures 40°. How many sides does the polygon have?

   (A) 6 (B) 8 (C) 9 (D) 12

2. A tabletop has the shape of a regular polygon. The measure of an internal angle of the tabletop is 135°. The tabletop is in the shape of a(n)

   (A) hexagon. (B) heptagon.

   (C) octagon. (D) nonagon.

3. The sum of the interior angles of a polygon is three times the sum of its exterior angles. How many sides are in the polygon?

   (A) 4 (B) 6 (C) 8 (D) 10

4. The figure below is a regular hexagon.

   What is the value of y?

   (A) 2 (B) 14 (C) 26 (D) 34

5. What is the measure of the *smallest* interior angle in the quadrilateral?

   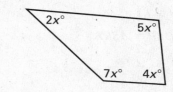

   (A) 20° (B) 40° (C) 80° (D) 140°

California Standards
Intensive Review

California Standards
Geometry 13.0

Angles and Polygons

Example

Prove Angles are Congruent

GIVEN ▶ $\overline{AB} \parallel \overline{DC}$, $\angle DFC$ is a right angle.
$\angle ADB$ is complementary to $\angle ABD$.

PROVE ▶ $\angle ADB \cong \angle DCF$

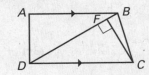

Solution

Statements	Reasons
1. $\overline{AB} \parallel \overline{DC}$, $\angle DFC$ is a right angle. $\angle ADB$ is complementary to $\angle ABD$.	1. Given
2. $m\angle ADB + m\angle ABD = 90°$	2. Definition of complementary angles
3. $m\angle ADB + m\angle ABD + m\angle DAB = 180°$	3. Triangle Sum Theorem
4. $90° + m\angle DAB = 180°$	4. Substitute.
5. $m\angle DAB = 90°$	5. Subtract.
6. $\angle DAB$ is a right angle.	6. Definition of right angle
7. $\overline{DA} \perp \overline{AB}$	7. Definition of perpendicular
8. $\overline{AD} \perp \overline{DC}$	8. Perpendicular Transversal Theorem
9. $\angle ADC$ is a right angle.	9. Definition of perpendicular
10. $m\angle ADC = 90°$	10. Definition of right angle
11. $\angle ADB$ is complementary to $\angle BDC$.	11. Definition of complementary angles
12. $\angle BDC$ is complementary to $\angle DCF$.	12. Acute angles of a right triangle are complementary.
13. $\angle ADB \cong \angle DCF$	13. Congruent Complements Theorem

Exercises

1. Which additional piece of information would be enough to find the measure of $\angle STR$?

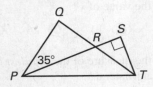

Ⓐ $\overline{QR} \cong \overline{RT}$

Ⓑ $\angle QRP \cong \angle SRT$

Ⓒ $\overline{QT} \perp \overline{PQ}$

Ⓓ $\overline{ST} \cong \overline{QR}$

2. For the figure below, which expression gives the correct value of y in terms of x?

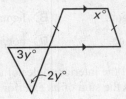

Ⓐ $y = \dfrac{x}{5}$

Ⓑ $y = 5x$

Ⓒ $y = \dfrac{180 - x}{5}$

Ⓓ $y = \dfrac{x + 90}{5}$

Name _____   Date _____

California Standards
Geometry 14.0, 15.0

Pythagorean Theorem

Example 1   **Find the Area of a Triangle**

On the map of a park's walkways, the distance from the fountain
to the rose garden is 62 feet, and the distance from the rose garden
to the playground is 136 feet. What is the area of the triangle
enclosed by these walkways?

Solution

STEP 1 Find the distance from the fountain to the
playground.

$$\left(\frac{\text{Distance from rose}}{\text{garden to playground}}\right)^2 = \left(\frac{\text{Distance from rose}}{\text{garden to fountain}}\right)^2 + \left(\frac{\text{Distance from fountain}}{\text{to playground}}\right)^2$$

$136^2 = 62^2 + x^2$	**Substitute.**
$18{,}496 = 3844 + x^2$	**Multiply.**
$14{,}652 = x^2$	**Subtract 3844 from each side.**
$\sqrt{14{,}652} = x$	**Find positive square root.**
$121 \approx x$	**Approximate with calculator.**

STEP 2 Find the area of the triangle.

$$A = \frac{1}{2}bh \approx \frac{1}{2}(62)(121) = 3751$$

Answer The area of triangle enclosed by the walkways is about 3751 square feet.

Exercises

1. Cory is building a rectangular frame. In order
to check that the frame has right angles at its
corners, he is measuring the diagonals of the
rectangle. To the nearest tenth, what should be
the length of the diagonals?

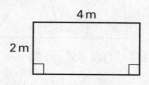

(A) 3.5 m   (B) 4.5 m

(C) 5.3 m   (D) 6.0 m

2. A slide is 6 feet high with
a horizontal base of 8 feet.
How long is the slide?

(A) 5.3 ft   (B) 10 ft

(C) 14 ft   (D) 16 ft

3. A diagonal bar on a gate is 10 feet long. If
the height of the gate is 2 feet, what is the
approximate length of the gate?

(A) 8 ft   (B) 9.8 ft

(C) 10.2 ft   (D) 12 ft

4. About how far is the lighthouse from the boat?

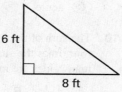

(A) 6.6 yd   (B) 11 yd

(C) 72.7 yd   (D) 90.4 yd

California Standards
Geometry 12.0, 13.0, 14.0, 15.0

Mixed Review

1. In the figure below, an exterior angle of the triangle measures 115°.

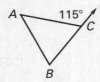

Which of the following could *not* be the measures of interior angles A and B?

(A) 35° and 80° (B) 40° and 75°

(C) 45° and 70° (D) 50° and 55°

2. The diagram shows the path Brandon walks from his home to school to the car wash where he works part-time after school. To the nearest tenth of a mile, how far does he walk from school to the car wash?

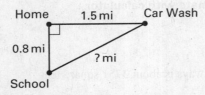

(A) 1.5 mi (B) 1.6 mi (C) 1.7 mi (D) 2.0 mi

3. The figure below is a regular pentagon.

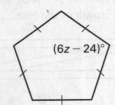

What is the value of z?

(A) 22 (B) 64 (C) 108 (D) 154

4. What is the value of y in the figure below?

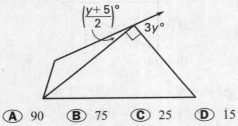

(A) 90 (B) 75 (C) 25 (D) 15

5. Arial has planted a new tree in her front yard. She is going to attach a rope that is 11 feet long to the tree and anchor it to the ground 8 feet from the base of the tree. How far up from the base of the tree should she attach the rope so that the tree will be held perpendicular to the ground?

(A) 13.6 ft (B) 7.5 ft

(C) 4.2 ft (D) 3.0 ft

6. The side lengths of a triangle are 8, x, and 17. If the length of the longest side is 17, what are the values of x that make the triangle acute?

(A) $9 < x < 15$ (B) $9 < x < 25$

(C) $15 < x < 17$ (D) $9 < x < 17$

7. What is the measure of the *largest* interior angle in the quadrilateral?

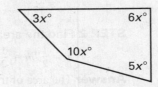

(A) 15° (B) 90° (C) 150° (D) 180°

8. In the figure below, the measures of ∠1, ∠2, and ∠3 are in a 3 : 4 : 5 ratio. What is the measure of ∠3?

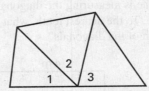

(A) 15° (B) 45° (C) 60° (D) 75°

9. What type of triangle has side lengths 6 feet, 11 feet, and 13 feet?

(A) right (B) isosceles

(C) acute (D) obtuse

10. The sum of the interior angles of a polygon is four times the sum of its exterior angles. How many sides are in the polygon?

(A) 4 (B) 6 (C) 8 (D) 10

11. The figure below shows a side view of the end support for a swing set. It was designed as an isosceles triangle. If the side of the support meets the ground at a 104° angle, what is the measure of the angle at the top of the support?

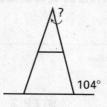

(A) 18° (B) 28° (C) 38° (D) 48°

12. The diagram below is part of a proof of the Pythagorean theorem.

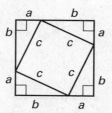

Which statement about the diagram would be used in the proof of the Pythagorean theorem?

(A) The four right triangles are congruent

(B) The area of the larger square is twice the area of the inner square.

(C) The perimeter of the larger square is $4(a + b)$.

(D) The perimeter of the inner square is $4c$.

13. What is the value of z in the figure below?

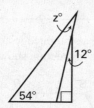

(A) 36 (B) 34 (C) 26 (D) 24

14. A construction worker rests a wooden board against a fence. The board is 12 feet long. The horizontal distance from the base of the fence to the end of the board is 3 feet. How high up the fence does the board reach?

(A) 12.4 ft   (B) 11.6 ft

(C) 10 ft   (D) 9 ft

15. What is the measure of an exterior angle of a regular octagon?

(A) 45° (B) 60° (C) 90° (C) 135°

16. An exterior angle of a regular polygon measures 30°. How many sides does the polygon have?

(A) 6   (B) 8   (C) 9   (D) 12

17. Jerome is building a storage shed in his back yard. He is going to use a 12-foot board to support one wall until he can fasten it. If he nails one end of the board 6 feet high on the wall, how far from the base of the wall will the other end of the support board need to be in order to form a right angle?

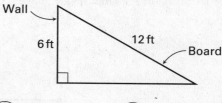

(A) 13.42 ft   (B) 11.18 ft

(C) 10.39 ft   (D) 6 ft

18. In the figure, the measure of ∠1 is 145°. What is the measure of ∠2?

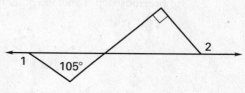

(A) 120° (B) 130° (C) 140° (D) 145°

19. The diagram shows an isosceles triangle with an altitude. What is the approximate area of the larger triangle?

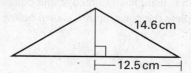

(A) 91.3 cm²   (B) 94.3 cm²

(C) 182.5 cm²   (D) 187.5 cm²

20. In triangle XYZ, $m\angle X = (2x + 11)°$, $m\angle Y = (3x - 2)°$, and $m\angle Z = (4x + 9)°$. Which of the following *best* describes triangle XYZ?

(A) scalene triangle   (B) equilateral triangle

(C) isosceles triangle (D) right triangle

California Standards
Intensive Review

California Standards
Geometry 16.0

Straightedge and Compass Construction

Example   ### Construct a Rhombus

Construct a rhombus using only a straightedge and a compass.

Solution

STEP 1

Using a straightedge, draw a segment $\overline{PS}$. Place the compass point on P and open it to the width of $\overline{PS}$. Draw an arc above $\overline{PS}$.

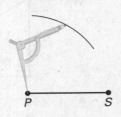

STEP 2

Label any point Q on the arc. Using the same compass setting, place the compass point at Q and draw an arc to the right of Q.

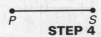

STEP 3

Place the compass point at S and draw an arc that intersects the arc drawn from Q in the previous step. Label the point of intersection R.

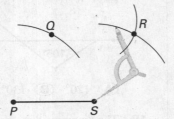

STEP 4

Using a straightedge, draw $\overline{PQ}$, $\overline{QR}$, and $\overline{RS}$.

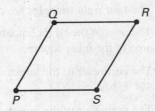

Exercises

1. Kevin is using a straightedge and compass to complete the construction shown below.

Which *best* describes the construction Kevin is completing?

(A) square

(B) equilateral triangle

(C) perpendicular bisector

(D) angle bisector

2. Jenny is using a straightedge and compass to complete the construction shown below.

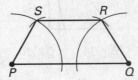

Which of the following *best* describes the construction Jenny is completing?

(A) trapezoid

(B) isosceles trapezoid

(C) parallel lines

(D) parallelogram

California Standards
Geometry 17.0

Coordinate Proofs

Example   **Write a Coordinate Proof**

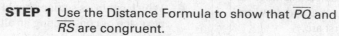

Prove that quadrilateral $PQRS$ is a parallelogram.

Solution

One way we can show that a quadrilateral is a parallelogram is to show that one pair of opposite sides is congruent and parallel.

STEP 1 Use the Distance Formula to show that $\overline{PQ}$ and $\overline{RS}$ are congruent.

$$PQ = \sqrt{[5 - (-1)]^2 + (3 - 5)^2} = \sqrt{40} = 2\sqrt{10}$$

$$RS = \sqrt{[0 - (-2)]^2 + (0 - 6)^2} = \sqrt{40} = 2\sqrt{10}$$

Since $PQ = RS = 2\sqrt{10}$, $\overline{PQ} \cong \overline{RS}$.

STEP 2 Use the slope formula to show that $\overline{PQ} \parallel \overline{RS}$.

Slope of $\overline{PQ} = \dfrac{3-5}{5-(-1)} = \dfrac{-2}{6} = -\dfrac{1}{3}$.

Slope of $\overline{RS} = \dfrac{0-(-2)}{0-6} = \dfrac{2}{-6} = -\dfrac{1}{3}$.

Since $\overline{PQ}$ and $\overline{RS}$ have the same slope, they are parallel.

$\overline{PQ}$ and $\overline{RS}$ are congruent and parallel, so quadrilateral $PQRS$ is a parallelogram.

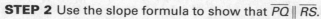

Exercises

1. In right triangle PQR, point P has coordinates $(a, 0)$ and point Q has coordinates $(0, b)$. Which of the following is *not* a possible set of coordinates for point R?

  A (a, b)

  B $(2a, b)$

  C $(0, 0)$

  D $(b, a + b)$

2. What is the midpoint of $\overline{KL}$?

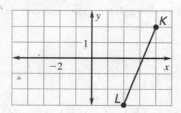

  A $\left(1, \dfrac{5}{2}\right)$ **B** $\left(-1, -\dfrac{5}{2}\right)$

  C $\left(3, -\dfrac{1}{2}\right)$ **D** $(6, -1)$

3. Figure $JKMN$ is a parallelogram.

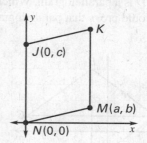

What are the coordinates of K?

  A $(a + c, b)$

  B $(b + c, a)$

  C $(a, b + c)$

  D $(b, a + c)$

4. A circle has the equation $(x + 2)^2 + (y + 1)^2 = r^2$. If point $(-2, 2)$ lies on the circle, what is the value of r?

  A 3   **B** 5   **C** 9   **D** 25

California Standards
Geometry 16.0, 17.0

Mixed Review

---

1. Which quadrilateral can be constructed by starting with the following steps?

> 1. Choose a compass setting greater than $\frac{1}{2}\,AC$. Place the compass point at A and draw an arc above $\overline{AC}$.
> 2. Without changing the compass setting, place the compass point at C and draw an arc that intersects the first arc.
> 3. Increase the compass setting. Place the compass point at A and draw an arc below $\overline{AC}$.
> 4. Without changing the compass setting, place the compass point at C and draw an arc that intersects the previous arc.

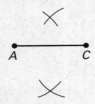

(A) kite   **(B)** parallelogram

(C) trapezoid   **(D)** rectangle

2. Figure $ABCD$ is a parallelogram. Which statement would prove that parallelogram $ABCD$ is a rhombus?

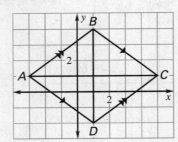

(A) $AB = CD$

(B) $AC = BD$

(C) slope $\overline{AB}$ = slope $\overline{CD}$

(D) $\left(\text{slope } \overline{AC}\right)\left(\text{slope } \overline{BD}\right) = -1$

3. Triangle ABC is formed by the points $A(-3, -2)$, $B(-1, 3)$, and $C(4, 1)$. Which of the following *best* describes the triangle?

(A) obtuse   **(B)** equilateral

(C) isosceles   **(D)** scalene

4. Which compass setting should you use in the next step of constructing an altitude of $\triangle ABC$?

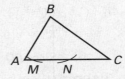

(A) a compass setting that is greater than $\frac{1}{2}\,MN$

(B) a compass setting that is less than $\frac{1}{2}\,MN$

(C) a compass setting that is equal to $\frac{1}{2}\,MN$

(D) a compass setting that is less than or equal to $\frac{1}{2}\,MN$

5. Sarah is using a straightedge and compass to complete the construction shown below. Which *best* describes the construction Sarah is completing?

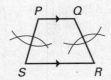

(A) parallelogram

(B) median of a trapezoid

(C) copying a segment

(D) line through a given point parallel to a given line

6. A circle has the equation $(x - 1)^2 + (y + 5)^2 = r^2$. If point $(4, -1)$ lies on the circle, what is the value of r?

(A) 5   **(B)** $\sqrt{61}$ **(C)** 9   **(D)** $\sqrt{85}$

California Standards
Intensive Review

7. In the diagram, quadrilateral *ABCD* is a parallelogram. What are the coordinates of point *M*?

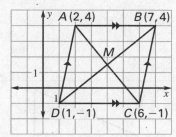

Ⓐ $\left(2, \frac{5}{2}\right)$

Ⓑ $\left(3, \frac{3}{2}\right)$

Ⓒ $\left(4, \frac{3}{2}\right)$

Ⓓ $\left(4, \frac{5}{2}\right)$

8. What is the equation of the line that passes through the point $(3, -2)$ and is perpendicular to line *m*?

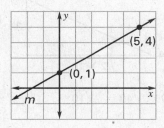

Ⓐ $3x + 5y = -1$

Ⓑ $5x + 3y = -1$

Ⓒ $3x + 5y = 9$

Ⓓ $5x + 3y = 9$

9. Figure *WXYZ* is an isosceles trapezoid. What are the coordinates of *X*?

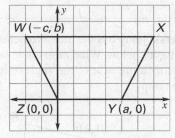

Ⓐ $(a, b + c)$ Ⓑ $(2a, b)$

Ⓒ $(a + c, b)$ Ⓓ $(a - c, b)$

10. The diagram shows triangle *PQR*. Which statement would prove that triangle *PQR* is a right triangle?

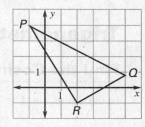

Ⓐ $(\text{slope } \overline{PR})(\text{slope } \overline{RQ}) = 1$

Ⓑ $(\text{slope } \overline{PR})(\text{slope } \overline{RQ}) = -1$

Ⓒ $\text{slope } \overline{PR} = \text{slope } \overline{RQ}$

Ⓓ $\text{slope } \overline{PR} \neq \text{slope } \overline{RQ}$

11. Which of the following is the equation of a line that passes through the point $(3, -3)$ and is parallel to the line $x + 3y = 6$?

Ⓐ $x + 3y = -2$

Ⓑ $x + 3y = -6$

Ⓒ $3x - y = 210$

Ⓓ $3x - y = 14$

12. The diagram shows parallelogram *FGHJ*. Which statement would prove that parallelogram *FGHJ* is a rectangle?

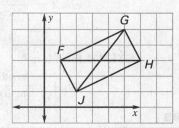

Ⓐ $FH = JG$

Ⓑ $FG = JH$

Ⓒ $(\text{slope } \overline{FH})(\text{slope } \overline{JG}) = 1$

Ⓓ $(\text{slope } \overline{FH})(\text{slope } \overline{JG}) = -1$

California Standards
Intensive Review

California Standards
Geometry 18.0

Trigonometric Functions

Example   **Find the Cosine and Tangent**

In the figure, $\sin A = \frac{3}{7}$. Find $\cos A$ and $\tan A$.

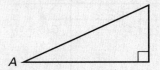

Solution

STEP 1 Label the sides of the triangle.

$$\sin A = \frac{3}{7} = \frac{\text{length of leg opposite } \angle A}{\text{length of hypotenuse}}$$

length of leg opposite $\angle A = 3$

length of hypotenuse $= 7$

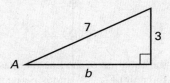

STEP 2 Use the Pythagorean theorem to find b.

$$a^2 + b^2 = c^2$$
$$b^2 = c^2 - a^2$$
$$b = \sqrt{c^2 - a^2} = \sqrt{7^2 - 3^2} = \sqrt{49 - 9} = \sqrt{40} = 2\sqrt{10}$$

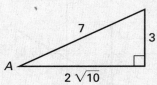

STEP 3 Find $\cos A$.

$$\cos A = \frac{\text{length of leg adjacent to } \angle A}{\text{length of hypotenuse}} = \frac{b}{7} = \frac{2\sqrt{10}}{7}$$

STEP 4 Find $\tan A$.

$$\tan A = \frac{\text{length of leg opposite } \angle A}{\text{length of leg adjacent to } \angle A} = \frac{3}{2\sqrt{10}} = \frac{3\sqrt{10}}{20}$$

Exercises

1. In the figure below, $\sin C = 0.4$. What is the length of $\overline{AC}$?

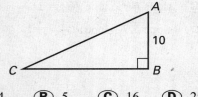

(A) 4   (B) 5   (C) 16   (D) 25

2. In right triangle PQR, $\angle Q$ is the right angle, $\sin R = \frac{8}{17}$, and $\cos R = \frac{15}{17}$. What is $\tan R$?

(A) $\frac{7}{15}$ (B) $\frac{8}{15}$ (C) $\frac{17}{8}$ (D) $\frac{15}{8}$

3. A waterski jump has the measurements shown in the figure below. What ratio could be used to find the measure of $\angle C$, the angle of inclination for the ramp?

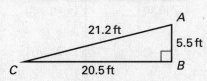

(A) $\cos C = \frac{5.5}{20.5}$ (B) $\cos C = \frac{5.5}{21.2}$

(C) $\sin C = \frac{5.5}{20.5}$ (D) $\sin C = \frac{5.5}{21.2}$

California Standards Intensive Review

California Standards
Geometry 19.0

Solving Right Triangles

Example   ### Use a Trigonometric Ratio to Find a Height

An airplane is at an altitude of 1.5 miles above sea level when it starts to climb at a constant angle of 2°. What is the altitude of the airplane after it has traveled 55 ground miles?

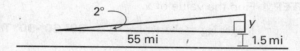

Solution

STEP 1 Find y.

$$\tan 2° = \frac{\text{opposite}}{\text{adjacent}}$$ **Write ratio for tangent of 2°.**

$$\tan 2° = \frac{y}{55}$$ **Substitute.**

$$55 \cdot \tan 2° = y$$ **Multiply each side by 55.**

$$y \approx 55 \cdot 0.0349$$ **Use a calculator to find tan 2°.**

$$y \approx 1.9$$ **Simplify.**

STEP 2 Find the altitude.

$$\text{altitude} = 1.5 + y \approx 1.5 + 1.9 \approx 3.4$$

Answer The airplane is at an altitude of about 3.4 miles above sea level after traveling 55 ground miles.

Exercises

1. In the figure below, a cable supports a radio tower. The tower is 385 feet tall. What is the approximate distance from the anchor point of the cable to the base of the tower?

$\sin 76° \approx 0.97$
$\cos 76° \approx 0.24$
$\tan 76° \approx 4.01$

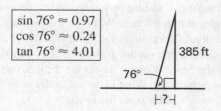

Ⓐ 93.1 ft   Ⓑ 96.0 ft

Ⓒ 373.6 ft   Ⓓ 396.8 ft

2. Triangle PQR is shown below.

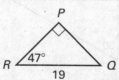

Which equation could be used to find PR?

Ⓐ $\sin 47° = \frac{19}{PR}$

Ⓑ $\cos 47° = \frac{19}{PR}$

Ⓒ $\sin 43° = \frac{PR}{19}$

Ⓓ $\cos 43° = \frac{PR}{19}$

California Standards
Intensive Review

California Standards
Geometry 20.0

Special Right Triangles

Example

Find the Lengths of the Hypotenuse and a Leg

Find the values of x and y. Write your answer in simplest radical form.

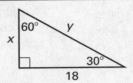

Solution

STEP 1 Find the value of x.

longer leg = shorter leg $\cdot \sqrt{3}$	**30°-60°-90° Triangle Theorem**
$18 = x\sqrt{3}$	**Substitute.**
$\dfrac{18}{\sqrt{3}} = x$	**Divide each side by $\sqrt{3}$.**
$\dfrac{18}{\sqrt{3}} \cdot \dfrac{\sqrt{3}}{\sqrt{3}} = x$	**Multiply numerator and denominator by $\sqrt{3}$.**
$\dfrac{18\sqrt{3}}{3} = x$	**Multiply fractions.**
$6\sqrt{3} = x$	**Simplify.**

STEP 2 Find the value of y.

hypotenuse = 2 $\cdot$ shorter leg	**30°-60°-90° Triangle Theorem**
$y = 2 \cdot 6\sqrt{3} = 12\sqrt{3}$	**Substitute and simplify.**

Exercises

1. What is the exact length of the short leg of the triangle shown here?

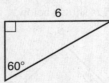

Ⓐ $6\sqrt{3}$ Ⓑ 3   Ⓒ $3\sqrt{3}$ Ⓓ $2\sqrt{3}$

2. What is the value of t in the triangle below?

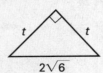

Ⓐ $\sqrt{6}$ Ⓑ $2\sqrt{2}$ Ⓒ $2\sqrt{3}$ Ⓓ $4\sqrt{3}$

3. In the figure below, what is x if $y = 10\sqrt{3}$?

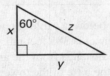

Ⓐ $5\sqrt{3}$ Ⓑ 5   Ⓒ 10   Ⓓ 15

4. Connor is standing on a step ladder that is set up right next to a fence. When he looks down at an angle of depression of 45°, he sees his younger sister playing on the ground on the other side of the fence. Conner's eyes are 12 feet from his younger sister. What is the exact distance of Conner's sister from the fence?

Ⓐ $4\sqrt{3}$ ft   Ⓑ $6\sqrt{2}$ ft

Ⓒ $12\sqrt{2}$ ft   Ⓓ $12\sqrt{3}$ ft

California Standards Intensive Review

Name _____   Date _____

1. In the diagram, a 16-foot board leans against the side of a barn. The board makes a 72° angle with the ground. Which of the following is closest to the distance from the bottom of the board to the base of the wall?

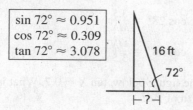

| sin 72° ≈ 0.951 |
| cos 72° ≈ 0.309 |
| tan 72° ≈ 3.078 |

16 ft

72°

⊢?⊣

(A) 4.9 ft   (B) 5.2 ft

(C) 10.4 ft   (D) 15.2 ft

2. In the figure below, $\sin A = \frac{2}{3}$ and $\tan A = \frac{2\sqrt{5}}{5}$. What is $\cos A$?

A

(A) $\frac{\sqrt{5}}{2}$ (B) $\frac{\sqrt{5}}{5}$ (C) $\frac{\sqrt{5}}{3}$ (D) $\frac{3\sqrt{5}}{5}$

3. Triangle ABC is a right triangle. What is the length of $\overline{BC}$?

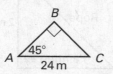

B

A 45°

24 m

C

(A) $24\sqrt{2}$ m   (B) $16\sqrt{3}$ m

(C) $12\sqrt{2}$ m   (D) $8\sqrt{3}$ m

4. In right triangle MQR, $\angle R$ is the right angle and $\sin Q = \frac{\sqrt{11}}{4}$. What is $\cos Q$?

(A) $\frac{4}{5}$

(B) $\sqrt{5}$

(C) $\frac{\sqrt{55}}{11}$

(D) $\frac{\sqrt{5}}{4}$

5. Which equation could be used to find the side length s in the triangle below?

s h s

60°

s

(A) $s = \frac{\sqrt{3}}{2} h$

(B) $s = \frac{\sqrt{2}}{2} h$

(C) $s = \sqrt{2} h$

(D) $s = \frac{2\sqrt{3}}{3} h$

6. In the figure below, $\tan B = \frac{9}{40}$.

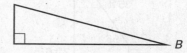

B

What are $\sin B$ and $\cos B$?

(A) $\sin B = \frac{40}{41}$ and $\cos B = \frac{9}{41}$

(B) $\sin B = \frac{9}{41}$ and $\cos B = \frac{40}{41}$

(C) $\sin B = \frac{9}{41}$ and $\cos B = \frac{41}{40}$

(D) $\sin B = \frac{41}{9}$ and $\cos B = \frac{41}{40}$

7. To the nearest hundredth, what is the length of $\overline{JK}$?

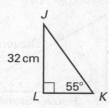

J

32 cm

55°

L K

(A) 18.35 cm

(B) 26.21 cm

(C) 39.06 cm

(D) 55.79 cm

8. In the figure below, $m\angle A = 36°$ and $AC = 9$. Which expression could be used to find the value of x?

Ⓐ $9 \sin 36°$ Ⓑ $\dfrac{9}{\sin 36°}$

Ⓒ $9 \tan 36°$ Ⓓ $\dfrac{9}{\tan 36°}$

9. Denise uses a large helium balloon to advertise the Booster Club car wash. She ties it to 35 feet of string, and the angle of inclination the balloon is making from the horizontal is about 56°. How high is the balloon above the ground if it is tied to the back of a chair at a point 2 feet 6 inches above the ground?

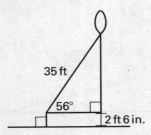

Ⓐ about 22.1 ft

Ⓑ about 31.5 ft

Ⓒ about 34.6 ft

Ⓓ about 54.4 ft

10. Three streets in a city form a right angle as shown in the figure below. To the nearest tenth, what is the length of Hoover Street?

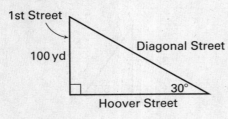

Ⓐ 57.7 yd   Ⓑ 122.5 yd

Ⓒ 173.2 yd   Ⓓ 200 yd

11. Right triangle MNP is shown below. Which equation could be used to find MN?

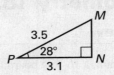

Ⓐ $\tan 62° = \dfrac{3.1}{MN}$

Ⓑ $\tan 62° = \dfrac{MN}{3.1}$

Ⓒ $\cos 28° = \dfrac{3.5}{MN}$

Ⓓ $\cos 28° = \dfrac{MN}{3.5}$

12. In the figure below, $\tan X = 0.7$. What is the length of $\overline{YZ}$?

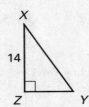

Ⓐ 4.9   Ⓑ 9.8   Ⓒ 10   Ⓓ 20

13. Raul has a square piece of wood on which he is painting two different scenes. He is planning to separate the two scenes with a piece of braided rope as shown below. About how many centimeters long will the braided rope need to be?

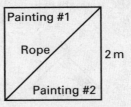

Ⓐ 400 cm   Ⓑ 388 cm

Ⓒ 321 cm   Ⓓ 283 cm

14. Triangle XYZ is shown below. Which equation could be used to find XZ?

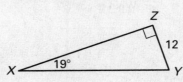

Ⓐ $\sin 19° = \dfrac{12}{XZ}$ Ⓑ $\tan 19° = \dfrac{12}{XZ}$

Ⓒ $\sin 19° = \dfrac{XZ}{12}$ Ⓓ $\tan 19° = \dfrac{XZ}{12}$

California Standards Intensive Review

Name _____ Date _____

California Standards
Geometry 21.0

Circles

Example 1 **Use Properties of Secants and Tangents**

Use the figure at the right to find BC.

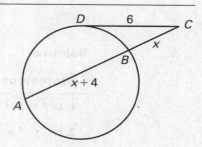

Solution

$$DC^2 = BC \cdot AC$$ **Write equation using Segments of Secants and Tangents Therorem.**

$$6^2 = x \cdot (x + (x + 4))$$ **Substitute.**

$$36 = x(2x + 4)$$ **Simplify.**

$$0 = 2x^2 + 4x - 36$$ **Write in standard form.**

$$0 = x^2 + 2x - 18$$ **Simplify.**

This expression is not factorable, so use the Quadratic Formula.

$$x = \frac{-b \pm \sqrt{b^2 - 4ac}}{2a}$$ **Quadratic Formula**

$$x = \frac{-2 \pm \sqrt{2^2 - 4(1)(-18)}}{2(1)}$$ $a = 1, b = 2, c = -18$

$$x = -1 + \sqrt{19} \text{ or } -1 - \sqrt{19}$$ **Lengths cannot be negative. Use the positive solution.**

$$x \approx 3.36$$ **Use a calculator.**

Answer $BC \approx 3.36$

Exercises

1. $\overline{WY}$ is a diameter of circle X and $\overline{YZ}$ is tangent to the circle at Y. What is $m\angle WXZ$?

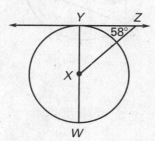

  Ⓐ 32°   Ⓑ 58°   Ⓒ 116°   Ⓓ 148°

2. In the figure below, secant $\overline{HK}$ intersects the circle at J and $\overline{GH}$ is tangent to the circle at G. If $KJ = 16$ and $JH = 4$, what is GH?

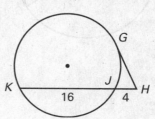

  Ⓐ $2\sqrt{5}$ Ⓑ 8   Ⓒ $4\sqrt{5}$ Ⓓ 12

California Standards
Intensive Review

Example 2

Use Properties of Inscribed Angles

GIVEN ► $\overset{\frown}{GH} \cong \overset{\frown}{LM}$, $\overset{\frown}{GK} \cong \overset{\frown}{KM}$
PROVE ► $\triangle GHK \cong \triangle MLK$

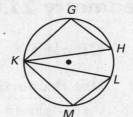

Solution

Statements	Reasons
1. $\overset{\frown}{GH} \cong \overset{\frown}{LM}$, $\overset{\frown}{GK} \cong \overset{\frown}{KM}$	1. Given
2. $m\overset{\frown}{GH} = m\overset{\frown}{LM}$, $m\overset{\frown}{GK} = m\overset{\frown}{KM}$	2. Definition of congruent arcs
3. $\frac{1}{2}m\overset{\frown}{GH} = \frac{1}{2}m\overset{\frown}{LM}$, $\frac{1}{2}m\overset{\frown}{GK} = \frac{1}{2}m\overset{\frown}{KM}$	3. Multiplication Property
4. $m\angle GKH = \frac{1}{2}m\overset{\frown}{GH}$, $m\angle MKL = \frac{1}{2}m\overset{\frown}{LM}$, $m\angle GHK = \frac{1}{2}m\overset{\frown}{GK}$, $m\angle KLM = \frac{1}{2}m\overset{\frown}{KM}$	4. Measure of an Inscribed Angle Theorem
5. $m\angle GKH = m\angle MKL$, $m\angle GHK = m\angle KLM$	5. Substitution
6. $\angle GKH \cong \angle MKL$, $\angle GHK \cong \angle KLM$	6. Definition of congruent angles
7. $\overline{GH} \cong \overline{LM}$	7. In the same circle, two minor arcs are congruent if and only if their corresponding chords are congruent.
8. $\triangle GHK \cong \triangle MLK$	8. AAS

Exercises

1. In circle D below, $\overline{AC}$ is a diameter and $m\angle CAB = 19°$. What is $m\overset{\frown}{AB}$?

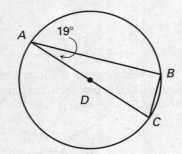

Ⓐ 38°

Ⓑ 71°

Ⓒ 142°

Ⓓ 161°

2. In the figure, quadrilateral $JKLM$ is inscribed in a circle. What is the value of a?

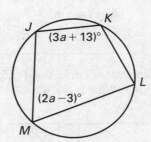

Ⓐ 16

Ⓑ 34

Ⓒ 38

Ⓓ 70

California Standards
Geometry 22.0

Transformations

Example

Rotate a Figure Using the Coordinate Rules

Graph figure *ABCDE* with vertices *A*(3, 4), *B*(7, 3), *C*(5, 0), *D*(2, −1), and *E*(1, 2).
Then rotate the quadrilateral 270° counterclockwise about
the origin.

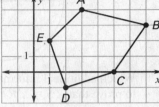

Solution

Graph *ABCDE*. Use the coordinate rule for a 270° rotation
to find the images of the vertices.

$$(a, b) \rightarrow (b, -a)$$

$$A(3, 4) \rightarrow A'(4, -3)$$

$$B(7, 3) \rightarrow B'(3, -7)$$

$$C(5, 0) \rightarrow C'(0, -5)$$

$$D(2, -1) \rightarrow D'(-1, -2)$$

$$E(1, 2) \rightarrow E'(2, -1)$$

Use the vertices to draw the image.

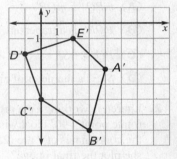

Exercises

1. The shortest distance between point *Y* and a line
   of reflection is 18 centimeters. What will be the
   distance between *Y* and its image *Y'*?

   (A) $3\sqrt{2}$ cm

   (B) 9 cm

   (C) 18 cm

   (D) 36 cm

2. Under a transformation, the image of point
   D(3, 1) is *D'*(1, −3). Which statement describes
   this transformation?

   (A) rotation of 90° counterclockwise

   (B) rotation of 270° counterclockwise

   (C) reflection over the *x*-axis

   (D) reflection over the *y*-axis

3. △*JKL* is transformed so that △*J'K'L'* has the
   coordinates *J'*(−4, −1), *K'*(−1, −2), and
   L'(−6, −5). What is the transformation?

   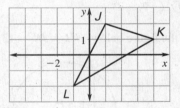

   (A) Translate △*JKL* 5 units left, 3 units down.

   (B) Rotate △*JKL* counterclockwise 180°.

   (C) Reflect △*JKL* across the *x*-axis.

   (D) Reflect △*JKL* across the *y*-axis.

California Standards
Intensive Review

California Standards
Geometry 21.0, 22.0

Mixed Review

1. Quadrilateral *PQRS* is inscribed in circle *C*.

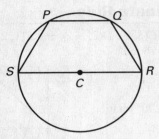

Which additional information would be enough to prove that $\angle S \cong \angle R$?

Ⓐ $m\overarc{PQ} = m\overarc{QR}$

Ⓑ *PQRS* is a trapezoid.

Ⓒ $PQ = \frac{1}{2}SR$

Ⓓ $\overline{SR}$ is a diameter of circle *C*.

2. Lauren is working on a problem where she must rotate point *J* 90° clockwise about the origin. If the coordinates of *J* are $(2, -7)$, where should she plot the final image?

Ⓐ $(2, 7)$

Ⓑ $(-2, 7)$

Ⓒ $(7, 2)$

Ⓓ $(-7, -2)$

3. In the figure below, $GH = JK = 13$.

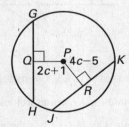

What is *PQ*?

Ⓐ 7

Ⓑ 5

Ⓒ 3

Ⓓ 2

4. In the figure, quadrilateral *QRST* is inscribed in a circle.

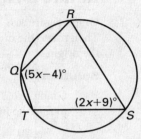

What is the value of *x*?

Ⓐ 25

Ⓑ 50

Ⓒ 59

Ⓓ 121

5. David translated $\triangle EFG$ 2 units to the right and 4 units down. What are the coordinates of the vertices of $\triangle E'F'G'$?

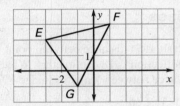

Ⓐ $E'(-5, -2), F'(-1, -1), G'(-3, -5)$

Ⓑ $E'(-1, -2), F'(3, -1), G'(1, -5)$

Ⓒ $E'(1, 0), F'(5, 1), G'(3, -3)$

Ⓓ $E'(-1, 6), F'(3, 7), G'(1, 3)$

6. Where is the image of $M(-3, 5)$ for the translation $(x, y) \rightarrow (x - 1, y + 3)$?

Ⓐ $(-4, 8)$

Ⓑ $(-2, 2)$

Ⓒ $(-2, 8)$

Ⓓ $(8, -4)$

California Standards
Intensive Review

7. In the figure below, secant $\overline{PQ}$ intersects the circle at R and secant $\overline{SQ}$ intersects the circle at T.

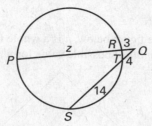

What is the value of z?

Ⓐ about 15.67   Ⓑ about 18.67

Ⓒ 21   Ⓓ 24

8. $\overline{JK}$ is a diameter of circle N and $\overline{MK}$ is tangent to the circle at K.

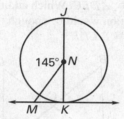

What is $m\angle KMN$?

Ⓐ 35°   Ⓑ 45°   Ⓒ 55°   Ⓓ 65°

9. In the figure, $\overline{XZ}$ and $\overline{VZ}$ are secants of circle C intersecting at Z.

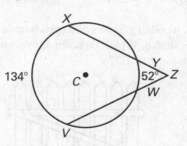

If $m\angle XZV = 52°$ and $m\widehat{XV} = 134°$, what is $m\widehat{WY}$?

Ⓐ 26°   Ⓑ 30°   Ⓒ 67°   Ⓓ 82°

10. In quadrilateral $RSTU$, the coordinates of R are $(3, -5)$. What are the coordinates of the image of R after a rotation 180° counterclockwise?

Ⓐ $R'(-3, -5)$ Ⓑ $R'(-5, -3)$

Ⓒ $R'(5, 3)$ Ⓓ $R'(-3, 5)$

11. In the figure below, $\overline{AB}$ is tangent to the circle at B and secant $\overline{AD}$ intersects the circle at C.

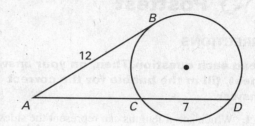

What is AC?

Ⓐ 5   Ⓑ 9   Ⓒ 13.6   Ⓓ 16

A quadrilateral with vertices $R(-3, -1)$, $S(-2, 3)$, $T(3, 4)$, and $U(4, 0)$ is reflected in the x-axis to obtain quadrilateral $R'S'T'U'$. What are the coordinates of S'?

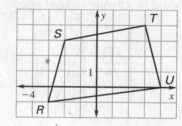

Ⓐ $(-2, -3)$

Ⓑ $(-2, -4)$

Ⓒ $(2, 3)$

Ⓓ $(2, -3)$

12. In the figure below, chord $\overline{PQ}$ intersects chord $\overline{ST}$ at R.

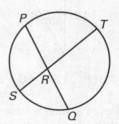

If $SR = 6$, $RT = 15$, and $PR = 9$, what is the length of $\overline{RQ}$?

Ⓐ 9   Ⓑ 10   Ⓒ 12   Ⓓ 22.5

California Standards
Intensive Review

California Standards
Posttest

DIRECTIONS

Read each question. Then, on your answer sheet, fill in the bubble for the correct answer.

1. Which set of lengths can represent the sides of a right triangle?

   (A) 5, 12, 13   (B) 7, 8, 10

   (C) 6, 6, 9   (D) 8, 12, 14

2. A 25.5-foot ladder rests against the side of a house at a point 24.1 feet above the ground. The foot of the ladder is x feet from the house. Find the value of x to one decimal place.

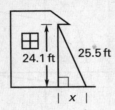

   (A) 1.9 ft   (B) 7.1 ft

   (C) 8.3 ft   (D) 10.1 ft

3. If c is $20\sqrt{2}$ in the right triangle below, what is the value of a?

   (A) $10\sqrt{2}$ (B) 12   (C) 25   (D) $4\sqrt{2}$

4. Two angles of a triangle have measures of 100° and 36°. Which of the following could *not* be a measure of an exterior angle of the triangle?

   (A) 136°   (B) 125°

   (C) 144°   (D) 80°

5. Which of the following figures *must* have four congruent angles?

   (A) parallelogram   (B) trapezoid

   (C) rectangle   (D) rhombus

6. In the figure below, n is a whole number. What is the *smallest* possible value for n?

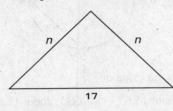

   (A) 8   (B) 16

   (C) 9   (D) 10

7. In the figure below, $\overline{AC} \cong \overline{CD}$, and $\angle ABC \cong \angle DEC$. Which additional information would be enough to prove that $\triangle ABC \cong \triangle CDE$?

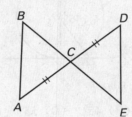

   (A) $\overline{AB} \cong \overline{ED}$ (B) $\angle B \cong \angle D$

   (C) $\angle E \cong \angle B$ (D) $\angle A \cong \angle D$

8. A wooden gate has z-shaped boards for support, as shown. Which theorem allows you to conclude that $\angle 1 \cong \angle 2$?

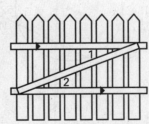

   (A) Alternate Interior Angles Theorem

   (B) Consecutive Interior Angles Theorem

   (C) Alternate Exterior Angles Theorem

   (D) Perpendicular Transversal Theorem

California Standards
Posttest *continued*

9. In the figure, Runway 3 crosses Runways 1 and 2 and acts as a transversal. Which pair of angles formed by the runways must be congruent?

Ⓐ ∠1 and ∠2   Ⓑ ∠2 and ∠4

Ⓒ ∠2 and ∠8   Ⓓ ∠5 and ∠6

10. In the diagram below, parallel lines *p* and *q* are cut by transversal *t*. Which statement about angles 1 and 2 *must* be true?

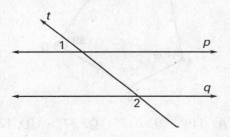

Ⓐ ∠1 is the supplement of ∠2.

Ⓑ ∠1 ≅ ∠2

Ⓒ ∠1 is the complement of ∠2.

Ⓓ ∠1 and ∠2 are right angles.

11. What is the length of the chord $\overline{PQ}$ in circle *C* below if the radius is 3 and the distance *d* to the center *C* is 2?

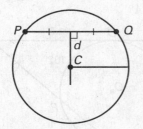

Ⓐ 5   Ⓑ $2\sqrt{5}$ Ⓒ $2\sqrt{13}$ Ⓓ 4

12. The figure shows a ramp leading up to a loading dock that forms a 15° angle with the ground. The loading dock height is 4 feet. What is the approximate distance from point *A* to point *B* to the nearest hundredth foot?

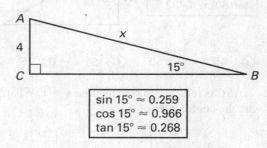

sin 15° ≈ 0.259
cos 15° ≈ 0.966
tan 15° ≈ 0.268

Ⓐ 4.14 ft   Ⓑ 14.93 ft

Ⓒ 15.45 ft   Ⓓ 26.67 ft

13. A straight slide 3.43 meters long makes an angle of 29° with the ground. About how much distance does the slide cover along the ground? Round to the nearest tenth.

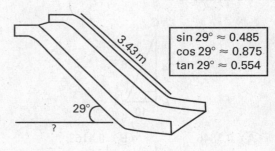

sin 29° ≈ 0.485
cos 29° ≈ 0.875
tan 29° ≈ 0.554

Ⓐ 3.4 m   Ⓑ 1.9 m

Ⓒ 1.7 m   Ⓓ 3.0 m

14. In the accompanying diagram, find the length of *x*.

sin 30° ≈ 0.5

cos 30° ≈ $\frac{\sqrt{3}}{2}$

tan 30° ≈ $\frac{\sqrt{3}}{3}$

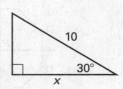

Ⓐ $5\sqrt{3}$ units   Ⓑ 5 units

Ⓒ $5\sqrt{2}$ units   Ⓓ 10 units

California Standard Posttest

California Standards
Posttest *continued*

15. Find the length of side *w*.

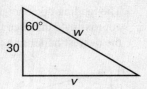

| sin 60° ≈ 0.866 |
| cos 60° ≈ 0.5 |
| tan 60° ≈ 1.732 |

A 45   **B** 60   **C** 55   **D** 75

16. △ABC is reflected across the line *x* = 1. What are the coordinates of *A′*?

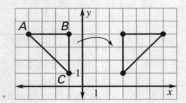

A (4, 6)   **B** (3, 4)   **C** (6, 4)   **D** (4, 3)

17. Find the sine of ∠A.

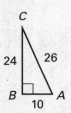

A 0.3846   **B** 0.4167
C 0.9231   **D** 1.0833

18. In the accompanying figure, which segment represents a 90° clockwise rotation of segment *AB* about *P*?

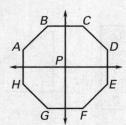

A $\overline{BC}$ **B** $\overline{EF}$
C $\overline{HG}$ **D** $\overline{CD}$

19. △ABC is to be reflected across the *y*-axis. What will be the coordinates of *B′*?

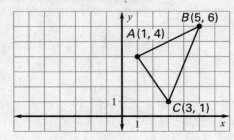

A (5, −6)   **B** (−1, 4)
C (−5, 6)   **D** (3, −1)

20. What is *m*∠ABC?

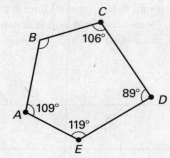

A 119°   **B** 117°   **C** 87°   **D** 125°

21. Which of the following is *not* a way to prove congruent triangles?

A SAS   **B** SSS
C ASA   **D** SSA

22. In the figure below, secant $\overline{AB}$ intersects circle *O* at points *P* and *Q*, $\overline{BD}$ is tangent to circle *O* at point *D*, $m\widehat{PD}$ =102°, and $m\widehat{DQ}$ =178°. What is *m*∠DBA?

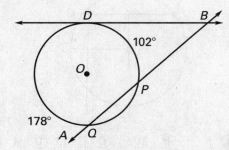

A 51°   **B** 89°   **C** 76°   **D** 38°

California Standards
Posttest continued

23. ∠1 and ∠2 are supplementary angles. ∠1 and ∠3 are vertical angles. If $m\angle 2 = 72°$, what is $m\angle 3$?

(A) 108°   (B) 72°

(C) 28°   (D) 18°

24. The length of the side of a regular nonagon is 3.4 centimeters. What is the radius of the nonagon?

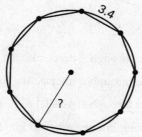

(A) 5 cm   (B) 3.4 cm

(C) 4 cm   (D) 8 cm

25. Given that the radius of the regular polygon below is 4.6 inches, what is the length of the side?

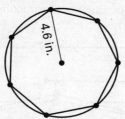

(A) 4.6 in.   (B) 4.0 in.

(C) 5.0 in.   (D) 3.5 in.

26. What are $m\angle EGD$ and $m\angle EDG$ in the inscribed figure?

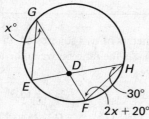

(A) 30° and 50°   (B) 60° and 50°

(C) 30° and 70°   (D) 60° and 70°

27. In the accompanying figure of a regular octagon, the radius is 4.0 units. What is the area of the inscribed circle? (radius of the circle = (radius of the octagon)(cos 22.5°), π = 3.14)

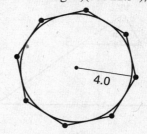

(A) 48.00 units²   (B) 12.56 units²

(C) 42.88 units²   (D) 50.24 units²

28. Which of the following facts would *not* be sufficient to prove that triangles ABC and DEF are similar?

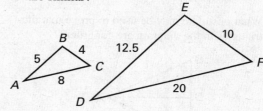

(A) ∠ACB is congruent to ∠DFE.

(B) ∠BAC is congruent to ∠EDF.

(C) Ratio of sides is 2.5 : 1.

(D) Each triangle is a scalene triangle.

29. What is the third congruence needed to prove that quadrilateral $ABCD$ is a parallelogram?

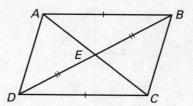

(A) $\overline{AE} \cong \overline{EC}$

(B) $\overline{AD} \cong \overline{DC}$

(C) $\overline{AB} \cong \overline{AD}$

(D) ∠DAB ≅ ∠BCD

California Standards
Posttest .continued

30. Triangle *WXY* is shown below where $\frac{AW}{YW} = \frac{BA}{XY}$. Which of the following must be true to prove that triangle *WXY* is similar to triangle *WBA*?

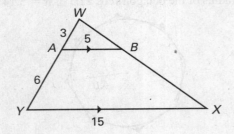

- **A** ∠*WBA* ≅ ∠*WXY*
- **B** $\overline{WB} \cong \overline{BX}$
- **C** $\frac{WB}{WX} = \frac{AW}{YW}$
- **D** $\frac{WB}{YX} = \frac{AW}{YW}$

31. What postulate may be used to prove that the triangles in the diagram are congruent?

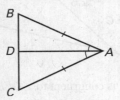

- **A** AA
- **B** SSS
- **C** SAS
- **D** ASA

32. What is the third congruence needed to prove that △*ABD* ≅ △*CBD* by AAS?

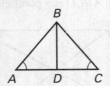

- **A** $\overline{AB} \cong \overline{BC}$
- **B** ∠*ABD* ≅ ∠*CBD*
- **C** $\overline{AD} \cong \overline{DC}$
- **D** ∠*DBA* ≅ ∠*CDB*

33. What type of triangle is formed by the points *A*(0, 0), *B*(0, 6), and *C*(4, 0)?

- **A** scalene triangle
- **B** isosceles triangle
- **C** right triangle
- **D** equilateral triangle

34. Eugene is using a straightedge and compass to do the construction below. Which *best* describes the construction Eugene is doing?

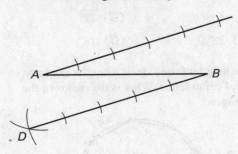

- **A** a line through *P* perpendicular to line *AB*
- **B** a line through *P* intersecting line *AB*
- **C** a line through *P* parallel to line *AB*
- **D** dividing line segment *AB* into 5 equal parts

35. Given three line segments as shown.

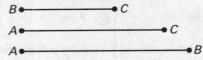

Which is not a step in constructing triangle *ABC*?

- **A**
- **B**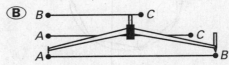
- **C** •*A*
- **D**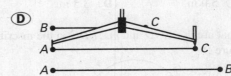

36. The perimeters of two squares are in a ratio of 5 to 11. What is the ratio between the areas of the two squares?

- **A** 15 to 33
- **B** 2 to 3
- **C** 5 to 11
- **D** 25 to 121

California Standards
Posttest *continued*

37. Greg is constructing a 45° angle using a straightedge and compass. He has completed three steps.

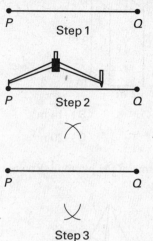

Which of the following is the next step?

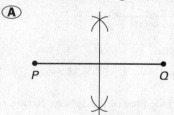

Ⓐ

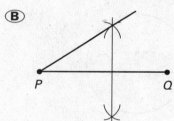

Ⓑ

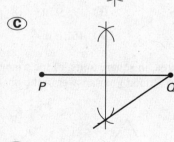

Ⓒ

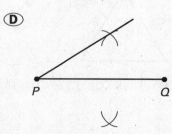

Ⓓ

38. If you used a compass to draw the bisector of ∠*ABC*, through which point would it pass?

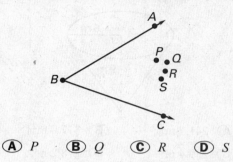

Ⓐ *P*   Ⓑ *Q*   Ⓒ *R*   Ⓓ *S*

39. What are the coordinates of the midpoint *M*?

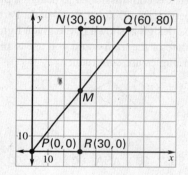

Ⓐ (40, 30)   Ⓑ (60, 40)

Ⓒ (30, 80)   Ⓓ (30, 40)

40. On a map, two cities are located at (2, 4) and (−2, 2). What is the distance between the cities on the map?

Ⓐ $2\sqrt{3}$ units   Ⓑ $2\sqrt{5}$ units

Ⓒ 12 units   Ⓓ 20 units

41. In the diagram below, $\overline{AB}$ = 19 units and $\overline{BC}$ = 40 units. Using the triangle inequality theorem, what is the maximum length $\overline{CA}$ needs to be to construct a triangle?

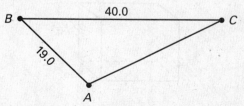

Ⓐ less than 59 units   Ⓑ more than 59 units

Ⓒ 59 units   Ⓓ less than 40 units

California Standard
Posttest

California Standards
Posttest *continued*

42. Find the surface area of the cone. Round to the nearest tenth.

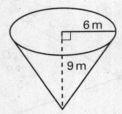

Ⓐ 241.7 m²   Ⓑ 317.0 m²

Ⓒ 239.4 m²   Ⓓ 278.2 m²

43. An artist is commissioned to design a piece of geometric artwork for the city park. Part of the artist's design is shown in the given figure. Which postulate or theorem could you use to prove the two triangles are congruent?

Ⓐ SSS   Ⓑ ASA   Ⓒ SAS   Ⓓ AAA

44. Find the volume of the prism shown.

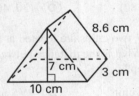

Ⓐ 110 cm³   Ⓑ 95 cm³

Ⓒ 105 cm³   Ⓓ 85 cm³

45. What is the surface area of the rectangular prism shown?

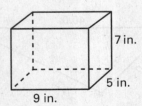

Ⓐ 68 in.²   Ⓑ 162 in.²

Ⓒ 227 in.²   Ⓓ 286 in.²

46. What is the volume of the right prism?

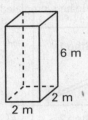

Ⓐ 24 m³   Ⓑ 14 m³

Ⓒ 10 m³   Ⓓ 20 m³

47. Find the volume of the pyramid. Round to the nearest tenth.

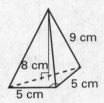

Ⓐ 141.4 cm³   Ⓑ 33.3 cm³

Ⓒ 47.1 cm³   Ⓓ 37.5 cm³

48. Find the surface area of the sphere. Round to the nearest tenth.

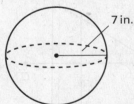

Ⓐ 307.8 in.²   Ⓑ 175.9 in.²

Ⓒ 615.8 in.²   Ⓓ 461.8 in.²

49. What is the area, in square units, of the triangle shown below? Round your answer to the nearest hundredth.

Ⓐ 5.20   Ⓑ 31.18   Ⓒ 12   Ⓓ 15.59

California Standard Posttest

California Standards
Posttest *continued*

50. What is the area of a square with a diagonal of 10 inches?

- (A) 50 in.^{2}
- (B) 25 in.^{2}
- (C) 56.6 in.^{2}
- (D) 100 in.^{2}

51. A large gazebo is shaped like a regular octagon. Its sides are 12 feet and it has an area of about 696 square feet. Find the area of a similar gazebo that has a side of length 8 feet. Round to the nearest tenth.

- (A) 130.5 ft^2
- (B) 309.3 ft^2
- (C) 116 ft^2
- (D) 1566 ft^2

52. Find the area of a triangle if the height is 6 inches and the base is 9 inches.

- (A) 7.5 in.^{2}
- (B) 18 in.^{2}
- (C) 15 in.^{2}
- (D) 27 in.^{2}

53. Given: *RMBS* is a rhombus. Which of the following *must* be true?

- (A) *RMBS* is a square.
- (B) Diagonals $\overline{RB}$ and $\overline{MS}$ are parallel.
- (C) $\overline{RM} \cong \overline{MB} \cong \overline{SR}$
- (D) *RMBS* is a rectangle.

54. Which congruence postulate could be used to prove $\triangle TRA \cong \triangle GRA$?

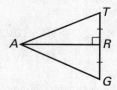

- (A) SAS
- (B) SSS
- (C) ASA
- (D) AAA

55. Suppose that the measures of the interior angles of a quadrilateral are $(2x - 1)°$, $(3x + 22)°$, $(x - 1)°$, and $(2x + 20)°$. What is the measure of the second largest angle?

- (A) 128°
- (B) 100°
- (C) 63°
- (D) 31°

56. Four exterior angles of a convex pentagon have measures 14°, 87°, 56°, and 30°. What is the measure of the fifth exterior angle?

- (A) 72°
- (B) 90°
- (C) 173°
- (D) 187°

57. "*If two triangles are both equilateral, then they are similar.*"

Which of the following best describes the *contrapositive* of the assertion above?

- (A) If two triangles are not both equilateral, then they are not similar.
- (B) Two triangles are similar if and only if they are both equilateral.
- (C) If two triangles are not similar, then they are not both equilateral.
- (D) If two triangles are similar, then they are both equilateral.

58. Use the proof to answer the question below.

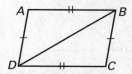

Given: $\overline{AB} \cong \overline{DC}$; $\overline{AD} \cong \overline{BC}$

Prove: $\angle A \cong \angle C$

Statement	**Reason**
$\overline{AB} \cong \overline{DC}$	Given
$\overline{AD} \cong \overline{BC}$	Given
$\overline{BD} \cong \overline{BD}$	Reflexive property
$\triangle ABD \cong \triangle CDB$	SSS
$\angle A \cong \angle C$	?

What reason can be used to prove $\angle A$ congruent to $\angle C$?

- (A) SAS
- (B) Corresponding angles of congruent triangles are congruent.
- (C) Opposite angles are supplementary.
- (D) Opposite angles are complementary.

California Standard Posttest

California Standards
Posttest *continued*

59. *"If a figure is round, then it is a circle."*

Which of the following best describes a *counterexample* to the statement above?

(A) A square is a figure.

(B) Spheres are round.

(C) A circle is a figure.

(D) Some figures are not round.

60. *"The sum of two numbers is always greater than at least one of the numbers."*

Which of the following best describes a *counterexample* to the statement above?

(A) $8 + (-4)$ (B) $6 + 0$

(C) $-2 + 1$ (D) $-3 + (-2)$

61. Use the proof to answer the question below.

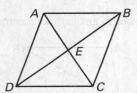

Given: *ABCD* is a parallelogram

Prove: $\triangle AED \cong \triangle CEB$

Statement	**Reason**
ABCD is a parallelogram.	Given
$\overline{AD} \cong \overline{BC}$	Opposite sides of parallelogram are congruent.
$\overline{AE} \cong \overline{CE}; \overline{DE} \cong \overline{BE}$	Diagonals of a parallelogram bisect each other.
$\triangle AED \cong \triangle CEB$	?

What reason can be used to prove $\triangle AED \cong \triangle CEB$?

(A) SAS   (B) AAA

(C) SSS   (D) ASA

62. A diagram from a proof of the Pythagorean theorem is pictured below

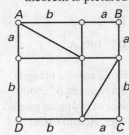 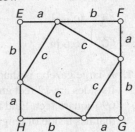

Which statement would *not* be used in the proof of the Pythagorean theorem?

(A) The area of $\square ABCD = \square EFGH$.

(B) area of $\square ABCD$: $4\left(\frac{1}{2}ab\right) + a^2 + b^2$

(C) area of $\square EFGH$: $4\left(\frac{1}{2}ab\right) + c^2$

(D) $ABCD \cong EFGH$

63. The figure below is a regular hexagon. What is the measure of each interior angle?

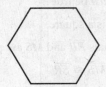

(A) 15°   (B) 60°   (C) 120°   (D) 30°

64. Which is the length of a diagonal of a square with side 10 inches long?

(A) $2\sqrt{5}$ in.   (B) $10\sqrt{2}$ in.

(C) 10 in.   (D) $5\sqrt{2}$ in.

65. The sum of the perimeters of a regular pentagon and a regular hexagon is 44. If the length of a side of the hexagon is equal to the length of a side of the pentagon, what is the length of a side of each polygon?

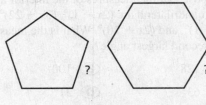

(A) 1   (B) 2   (C) 3   (D) 4